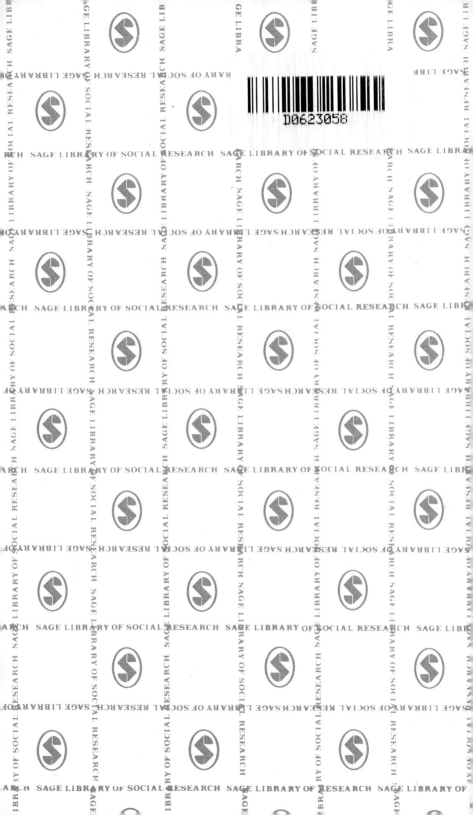

D0623058

THE PRACTICE OF URBAN ECONOMICS

Volume 107, Sage Library of Social Research

SAGE LIBRARY OF SOCIAL RESEARCH

THE PRACTICE OF
URBAN
ECONOMICS

Alfred J. Watkins

Foreword by **Wilbur R. Thompson**

Volume 107
SAGE LIBRARY OF
SOCIAL RESEARCH

 **SAGE PUBLICATIONS**   Beverly Hills   London

For information address:

SAGE Publications, Inc.
275 South Beverly Drive
Beverly Hills, California 90212

SAGE Publications Ltd
28 Banner Street
London EC1Y 8QE, England

Printed in the United States of America

Library of Congress Cataloging in Publication Data

Watkins, Alfred J.
 The practice of urban economics.

 (Sage library of social research ; v. 107)
 Bibliography: p.
 1. Urban economics—United States.
2. Cities and towns—United States—Growth.
I. Title.
HT321.W38   330.973'0926'091732   80-13809
ISBN 0-8039-1380-X
ISBN 0-8039-1381-8 (pbk.)

FIRST PRINTING

CONTENTS

ACKNOWLEGMENTS

This book is a revised version of my doctoral dissertation submitted to The Graduate Faculty of the New School for Social Research. Many faculty members and fellow graduate students in the Department of Economics aided greatly in the initial development of these ideas. In particular, I wish to thank Dr.Thomas Vietorisz, who served as my dissertation supervisor and close personal friend. Dr. David Gordon and Dr. Robert Heilbroner were not only generous with their time and advice, but were also instrumental in maintaining an intellectual environment conducive to critical inquiry. Paul Hancock and Robert Mier provided assistance with various theoretical and conceptual problems during the early stages of this research project. In addition, I wish to express my deep appreciation to Dr. David Perry of the Department of Government at the University of Texas, whose friendship, support, and advice were invaluable throughout the process of writing and revising this manuscript. My many colleagues, friends, and students at the University of Texas offered much needed support and companionship and, in addition, provided me with the opportunity to observe firsthand the growth of the Sunbelt. Dr. Karl Schmitt, chairman of the Department of Government, and Dean Robert King of the College of Liberal Arts provided assistance and financial support during various stages of this research. I also wish to thank Dr. William Livingston, Vice President and Dean of Graduate Studies at the University of Texas, for a grant to defray the costs of preparing the final draft of this manuscript. The constant encouragement and friendship of Charles Ulrich, Arnold Fleischmann, Robert Haley, Linda Moran, and Gary Kline made the task of research and writing much more pleasant. Finally, but by no means last, I would like to thank Kelly McWhirter for her friendly and efficient assistance in typing the manuscript and Kathy Eckstein, who converted often illegible diagrams into works of art.

–A.J.W.

FOREWORD

Before urban economics was "discovered" a couple of decades ago, cities, seen as local economies, were in the relevant literature little more than arbitrary, anonymous places where industries were located and where the gross national product just happened to be produced. One was in fact usually left with the impression that the GNP was actually produced at the national level, not just added up and reported out from the summit. With the rise of formal study in urban economics came close attention to the many and varied local forces—internal processes—that acted to generate more or higher-quality growth in some places than in others. Export bases, local multipliers, import substitution growth, agglomeration processes came to be commonplace concepts and even invaded the writings of journalists. Some even dared to flirt with the possibility that some places—some local economic environments—were capable of generating higher propensities to invent and innovate than were other places with different sets of industries, occupations, institutions, and economic histories.

In the exuberance of its intellectual puberty, urban economists, urban geographers, and development planners often overstated the degree to which a city was indeed a significantly autonomous local economy and substantial master of its own destiny. The author of this work does therefore perform a most useful service by forcing the discussion of industry location and urban growth theory back into direct and close contact with the national economy, but this time in a much longer timeframe and in the more demanding context of history. National economic and technological events and epochs create, promote, and suppress local growth and development in this far-reaching reinterpretation of the complex interaction between industries and cities.

But depicting cities as mere stages on which, one after another, national performances go on tour will surely attract the attention if not raise the hackles of many readers, even if they find much of the author's argument plausible to convincing. Many will wish to preserve a greater role for localism—for local history, pride, and loyalty—and not see cities as just pale reflections of the current state of national technology, resource availabilities, consumer taste patterns, or pervasive lifestyles. The whole would seem to be the sum of its parts, even if it is more than that. But both the readers and the author will be richer for the discourse that will surely arise.

Other readers will feel that this new interpretation of business location theory and practice, and especially one that is heavily weighted with examples from manufacturing, slights the growing importance of not just the service industries (in this "postindustrial age") but also the growing locational power of amenity-seeking households. Arguments why new (manufacturing?) industries will seek to locate in new cities rather than replace old industries in old cities may well add a fresh dimension to the discourse but fall short of explaining why nonmetropolitan areas have been growing at one and one-half times the metropolitan area growth rate through the 1970s.

This very serious and scholarly work weaves industrial location theory and practice together with the process of urban growth and development and deserves to be read carefully by students of this subject matter on its purely academic merits alone. But the most valuable feature of this book may well prove to be that it stimulates the reader to argue with the author, in part over the internal consistency of his logic but even more over his interpretation of recent national and regional economic history and its relevance to the future. The reader may come to wish that these pages had not been bound but had instead been offered in a loose-leaf, ring-binder notebook so that new pages on energy trends, new roles for women, birth-rate swings, politics, and world trade could be added to amend each "last word" on the nature of locational decisions and urban growth processes.

In a world that is changing as rapidly as this one, few ideas can expect to achieve immortality—probably none in the urban social sciences—and if therefore the reader is challenged to enter the game of intellectual leapfrog, the author will have succeeded as a teacher. In the world of ideas too, "the King is dead, long live the King."

In essence, what more attractive recommendation for this book can be made than to promise the reader that he will be prompted on its reading to revise his position on the matters at issue, irrespective of the degree to which he accepts the author's argument.

Wilbur R. Thompson
Wayne State University

Chapter 1

AN INTRODUCTION TO UNEVEN DEVELOPMENT

Nearly twenty-five years ago, the *New York Times Magazine* described the status of New York City in the following glowing terms:

> This island [Manhattan] will, for as many years as we can see ahead, be the hub of New York, the cynosure of visiting eyes, the crux of high values and congestions, the magnet which attracts those who seek . . . the finest of fine arts, the best of music, the latest in radio and television, the busiest and most modern medical centers. Here are the most luxurious shops with cargoes more fabulous than the gold and silver, precious stone, ivory, apes and peacocks brought to Solomon by the natives of Ophir and Tarshish. Here too, are the choicest foods, the biggest buildings, and most fabulous hotels and homes, the centers of management and finance, the oldest remaining slums and the newest mass housing. . . . Ours is a town of superlatives.[1]

At that time, New York City represented the social, cultural, and economic apex of the nation. New York's prominence was considered the symbol of U.S. economic development and the nation's position as the unchallenged master of the capitalist world.

Today, the *New York Times Magazine,* along with other popular and scholarly journals, emphasize a different theme. The superlatives which they now use to describe New York City and other major urban centers in the Northeast, do not highlight the positive features but only the seamier side of urban life. They argue that New York, along with most other metropolitan areas in the Northeast, are "dead" or "dying." A recent article in the same magazine that was so optimistic more than two decades ago suggests that in order to rejuvenate New York City, we must allow it to shrink. The author, Roger Starr, proposes selective neighborhood triage whereby certain sections of the city will be systematically encouraged to self-destruct and disappear.

According to Starr, we must begin to contemplate shrinkage and economic decline because this is the fate that has been prescribed by that ultimate arbiter of all economic decisions, the Invisible Hand.

> Part of the city's problem is that its exports have lost their attraction; in some industries like beer, the city's once thriving production has shrunk to exactly nothing. In others, like apparel, printing, and baking, the city's production for export and even for its own use has diminished drastically. Even much of the nighttime television production, once a New York monopoly, has moved to California.[2]

Thus, where just a few years ago scholars, politicians, and journalists displayed unbridled optimism about the health of the Northeastern cities, today they are attempting to devise policies to cope with economic decay. As the evidence of an urban crisis became more apparent, the dramatic turn of phrase employed by these analysts became more apocalyptic. In the past few years, the older northeastern central cities have been equated to a child's "sandbox"[3] or an Indian "reservation"[4] designed to house only society's misfits. More recently, William Baer coined the ultimate adjective. He suggests that some cities are "dead" and therefore they have become cemeteries.[5] He offers his cemetery thesis in order to stimulate contemplation about the "inevitable" and "natural" process of urban death. For too long, Baer argues, urban scholarship and domestic public policy have refused "to admit that older cities and neighborhoods can die; they may be 'sick' or 'deteriorating' but the belief is nevertheless held by experts and politicians alike that with proper treatment, these areas will recover and live forever." As a result, the time has come "to contemplate the various aspects of urban death and to suggest what may be done to ameliorate its consequences. Contemplation is meant to be just that: a considered exposition that treats urban death as very much in the natural order of things, to be taken in stride."[6]

Despite the publicity accorded the proponents of neighborhood and urban death, another group of scholars, the convergence theorists, argue that the Invisible Hand operates in a much more benign fashion.[7] From their perspective, cities are not dying. Instead, some of the older ones are merely laboring under the handicaps imposed by an economic system adjusting to a new spatial equilibrium. Spurred on by the greater productive efficiency emanating from cheap land, low wages, low taxes, and a "favorable business climate" and led by Houston, "the shining buckle of the Sunbelt," these newer cities are completing the inevitable process of convergence initiated before the turn of the century.

Generally speaking, the proponents of convergence argue that the Northeast's urban areas are not handicapped by some fatal, chronically debilitating illness. Instead their problems arise because the mantle of growth has temporarily shifted to those metropolitan areas with a more favorable constellation of factor costs. However, once a state of equilibrium is reestablished between the two regions, the extreme growth disparities can be expected to level off and all cities will grow in a more harmonious and uniform fashion. Unfortunately, this equilibrating, convergence process is not painless—the rich, more developed region will be made slightly poorer as the poor and less developed region becomes richer. Thus, according to these theorists, the present problems in the Northeast are not necessarily the harbingers of an alarming state of crisis. Rather they only reaffirm the existence of a self regulating market mechanism.

Upon closer examination, however, it is not at all clear what is meant by convergence. What exactly is converging in the two regions? Does convergence imply that the two regions are developing homogeneous industrial structures or is it simply a statement that the levels of development within the two regions are becoming more equal? Finally, what is the process by which the poor region begins to overtake its more developed counterpart?

According to its most accepted usage, convergence implies an increasing uniformity in various macrolevel indicators—i.e., per capita income, growth rates, factor costs, the sectoral distribution of the labor force, etc. Most of the empirical evidence seems to lend at least some credence to these hypothesized trends.[8] Regional differences in per capita income have been narrowed, factor cost differentials, while not totally eliminated, have been reduced, and those areas whose economic base had previously been dominated by agricultural pursuits have shifted to a more balanced industrial foundation. If this is the meaning of convergence, there is little to quibble over. Also, on a socio-cultural level, there is little doubt that regional peculiarities are moderating. Radio, television, and the cinema have all had a leavening effect. Within the Sunbelt, the shift of manufacturing plants from scattered rural locations to larger urban centers brought the tempo of life into greater accord with that of the more industrialized Northeast. And finally, the general flow of population from rural to urban areas has meant that small town values have been diffused by the more cosmopolitan outlook of metropolitan America. Thus, on this level also convergence is a meaningful concept.

But how does convergence occur? Certainly, the proponents of convergence do not wish to imply that Sunbelt cities are developing industrial structures that are carbon copies of northeastern cities. Although income levels and occupational distributions are becoming more similar, it would be ludicrous to argue that Tampa, Phoenix, and Las Vegas are, in some qualitative sense, similar to Philadelphia, Newark, and Akron. Moreover, it is rather doubtful that the present political and economic leaders of Houston or Austin are advocating that their respective cities emulate some of the better known qualities of New York City such as municipal bankruptcy, a shrinking economic base, outmigration, and gutted neighborhoods. It is clear, therefore, that in certain contexts the notion of convergence remains a relatively valid concept. Within other contexts, however, convergence is totally inapplicable.

On a more theoretical level, convergence theory rests upon the dual set of beliefs that (1) there exists a persistent tendency for the economies of two regions to conform to the conditions associated with a long run general equilibrium, and that (2) any forces that disturb the system will be offset by equal and opposite counteracting pressures. However, this vision of equilibrium has been rejected by Myrdal and replaced by a scenario that emphasizes the process of uneven development and deviation amplifying feedback cycles. According to Myrdal, "the system is by itself not moving toward any sort of balance between forces but is constantly on the move away from such a situation. In the normal case, a change does not call forth countervailing changes but, instead, supporting changes, which move the system in the same direction as the first change but much further."[9]

Myrdal's scenario postulates that within an urban setting, population and economic changes gain momentum as a change in one variable induces similar changes in the other variables. For example, when a local industry faces a sudden increase in demand, the local demand for labor grows and this encourages migrants to enter the region. But with more people and purchasing power concentrated in one area, new businesses appear and old ones expand. This produces additional employment opportunities and continuing inmigration. As a result, the attractiveness of the metropolitan area as a business location remains high and the city continues to grow. A similar growth spiral could also be ignited with the same cumulative effect either through the infusion of a new dynamic industry into the local economy (for example, petrochemicals in Houston; meat packing in

Kansas City and Omaha; or automobiles in Detroit) or through a change in the location propensity of an industry away from a dispersed pattern and toward a more nucleated arrangement (the agglomeration tendencies of the iron and steel industry starting in the mid-nineteenth century). In either case, the exogenous stimulus would increase the demand for labor and initiate a process of cumulative growth.

In declining metropolitan areas, simply failing to grow at a sufficiently rapid pace may inaugurate cumulative decline. Local industries, by not expanding, fail to create a high demand for labor. New entrants into the labor force must look elsewhere for employment and migrate from the region. With the ensuing population decline, the metropolitan area appears less attractive as a potential location, and already established firms, faced with a loss of markets, are forced to shut down. As local employment shrinks, outmigration accelerates, leading to additional business deaths. By then, the cumulative decline becomes firmly entrenched. Since it is a mathematical truism that the growth of some metropolitan regions at an above-average rate must be accompanied by the growth of other areas at a below-average rate, we can see that the process of cumulative causation and deviation amplifying feedback cycles will create uneven metropolitan development. If this scenario provides an accurate protrayal of urban dynamics, then the concept of long-run stable equilibrium must be discarded. Cities on disparate growth trajectories are not headed toward some common point but, on the contrary, are moving further away from each other. As a result, those empirical studies that demonstrate regional convergence ignore the dynamic qualities of economic evolution. Rather than convergence, a more appropriate analogy would be two trains headed in opposite directions. Up to a certain point the trains converge, but they will not stop once they have met. Instead, the process of convergence is merely a prelude to increasing divergence.

Therefore, studies which demonstrate that per capita incomes, industrial structure, and labor force participation rates are all converging and creating a relatively homogeneous system of cities are guilty of two misconceptions. First, they only capture the first half of the process—that portion which is relevant until the two trains meet. Second, they employ the technique of comparative statics. Statistics for two groups of cities are compared at two different times but the direction and cause of the long run secular trends are ignored. Yet to understand urban dynamics, we must focus explicitly on both the paths and causes of motion.

Moreover, even if we accept the existence of a long-run general equilibrium, this situation would not necessarily negate the concept of uneven development. With respect to the equilibrating tendencies that operate in a supply and demand situation, Lowe asserts:

> The terminal state of equilibrium which the law predicates is by no means identical with the initial one: the forces stimulated by the initial disturbance are supposed to respond to . . . an increase in demand not by a countervailing decrease in demand but by an increase in supply. As a consequence, the micro-structure of the terminal equilibrium differs characteristically from that of the initial equilibrium . . . by a change in the relative distribution of inputs and outputs over the sectors of production.[10]

In other words, any exogenous shock administered to a system will induce a permanent alteration in the system-defining parameters. As Lowe indicates, there can be no analogy between economic equilibrium and mechanical equilibrium. For example, a pendulum that is displaced from its place of rest will return eventually to its initial position. The force of gravity nullifies any other forces that disturb the system. In the realm of economics, however, the equilibrating forces do not counteract the initial shock. Instead, the economic system adapts to the shock by adjusting the other relevant parameters.

If Lowe's analysis is correct, then any equilibrating forces that operate within the system of cities will only widen the gap between growing and declining centers. Those cities that are disturbed by inmigration adjust by increasing the volume of economic activity while, conversely, declining cities adapt by reducing the level of economic activity. For both groups of cities, the terminal state will be different from the initial state and the adjustment process will only widen the disparities. Therefore, whether one argues from a paradigm of general equilibrium or from a paradigm based on deviation-amplifying feedback cycles, the end result is cumulative causation and uneven development.

BASIC OUTLINE

On an elementary level, the concept of urban and regional uneven development implies that capital accumulation and the location of rapidly growing industries are not dispersed evenly throughout the nation. Instead, these activities agglomerate in a few cities and metropolitan areas. This absence of spatial diffusion creates the phenomenon of prosperous and depressed regions. However, since the growth process is cumulative and self-reinforcing, those activities that have gained a head start will soon outstrip their rivals in terms of economic growth and employment. The laggards, on the other hand, will languish precariously between a state of slow growth and accelerating decline.

A general, theoretical overview, however, does not constitute an explanation. To provide this essential element, it is necessary to understand both the factors governing the spatial distribution of economic activity and the dynamics of urban growth. The following chapters will provide a critical analysis of several major theories that dominate the practice of urban economics and purport to explain why some cities grow while others decline. Each chapter will explore one theoretical approach in an attempt to elucidate those aspects which contain useful insights and to reconstruct other elements that can provide cogent explanations after some modifications of their static perspective. My aim in reviewing these neoclassical theories is neither to disparage nor discredit them, but simply to discuss critically their strengths and weaknesses and, in the process, establish a more solid analytic foundation that is both theoretically plausible to scholars and practically useful to policy analysts.

The traditional theories that will be considered can be divided into two broad categories. The first group contains several static or microlevel theories that describe the behavior of individual economic units (firms, industries, or cities) as they adjust to the dictates of a market-imposed competitive spatial equilibrium. The second category contains several dynamic or macrolevel theories that trace the evolution of specific cities from small settlements to major metropolitan centers.

Chapter 2 discusses the least cost theory of location. This approach views the site selection process in terms of cost minimization and emphasizes such variables as labor costs, transport costs, and agglomeration economies. Chapter 3 considers a second branch of location theory as well as central place theory. This second approach, which derives from duopoly theory, views the site selection process in terms of market areas and revenue maximization. In this approach, location decisions are predicated upon the assumption that location conveys an element of market control. Therefore, a firm's location depends upon the location of competitors and the spatial distribution of consumers. With this in mind, a firm tries to find a location that maximizes the firm's spatial monopoly and total revenue. While the revenue maximization formulation considers the locational interdependence of several firms in the same industry, central place theory analyzes the locational interdependence of cities. The theory assumes the existence of a region filled with cities and proceeds to investigate the market area forces scattering some activities throughout the central place system as well as the forces concentrating other activities in only the highest ranking members of the system of cities.

Thus, Chapter 2 and Chapter 3 form an integrated analysis of those theories that seek to explain the spatial distribution of economic activity. With very few exceptions, however, these theories do not consider explicitly the process of urban growth and decay. Chapter 4 bridges this gap by presenting one element of the urban growth literature. The basic vs. nonbasic industries debate ignores the spatial arrangement of industries and instead investigates the growth-inducing qualities of various economic activities. It divides the urban industrial structure into two segments: those industries whose products are exported are termed "basic" while those industries that service the export sector are denoted as "nonbasic." Generally, it is assumed that the expansion of the basic sector promotes urban growth while the nonbasic sector passively adjusts its output to conform to the needs of the basic industries. Thus, according to this view, the issue of the urban growth and decay can be reduced to an analysis of the dynamic impact of each city's basic activities. Based on the spatial distribution of expanding and shrinking basic industries, we can determine the spatial distribution of growing and declining urban areas. But in the opinion of another group of theorists, the basic sector is rather ephemeral and in a constant state of flux. The city's long-run economic viability, therefore, does not depend on a particular set of basic industries. Instead, prosperity is a function of the nonbasic industries since these affect the city's ability to attract new, high-quality basic activities.

None of the theories considered so far analyzes the process of urban growth. Instead, the discussion has been confined to an analysis of the location propensities of various firms and the ability of certain industries to stimulate urban growth. Therefore, Chapter 5 presents two traditional dynamic models of urban growth. The first suggests that cities pass through various stages as they ascend the urban hierarchy. The second focusses on the different economic activities that promoted city growth and new city formation during the mercantile and industrial eras. This model claims that cities do not pass through various stages but rather, it is the national economy that evolves and alters the composition of city-building activities.

Unfortunately, most of these dynamic models never discuss the mechanisms that first reduce a city's rate of growth and later produce absolute contraction. In view of this serious omission, there is a clear need for a new model that includes urban decay as an integral component of urban dynamic theory.

The next two chapters develop this model by tracing the process of uneven development through the three distinct waves of
capital accumulation that influenced the evolution of the U.S.
economy. Chapter 6 presents a general model of uneven urban
development that links the evolution of the U.S. economy to
the process of urban growth, stagnation, and decay. Chapter 7
builds upon the general model of uneven development and
traces the history of the U.S. system of cities through three
distinct phases of capital accumulation. During the mercantile
phase, national and urban prosperity were defined in terms of
the success or failure of various commercial ventures and their
ancillary, generally craft-based manufacturing activities. Once
this phase of capital accumulation had spent its developmental
potential, a new epoch emerged to carry the national economy
to new heights of prosperity. This second developmental era
was based on the creation of the capital infrastructure needed
to carry the industrial revolution to completion. During this
second epoch, commercial activities did not disappear nor did
they lose their importance in some older cities. They simply
receded into the background and generally were no longer
capable of serving as the foundation for the prosperity of the
newly emerging urban centers. This cyclical pattern was
repeated a third time when the industrial epoch gave way to a
new constellation of dynamic activities founded upon the pillars
of mass consumption, services, and the military-industrial complex. The present phase is often identified by the euphemisms—
"the post-industrial society" and "the rise of the Sunbelt."

NOTES

1. Quoted in Oliver C. Cox, *The Foundations of Capitalism* (New York: Philosophical Library, 1959): 14.
2. Roger Starr, "Making New York Smaller," *New York Times Magazine*
(November 14, 1976): 33.
3. George Sternlieb, "The City As Sandbox," *The Public Interest* 25 (Fall
1971): 14-21.
4. Norton Long, "The City as Reservation," *The Public Interest* 25 (Fall 1971):
22-38.

5. William C. Baer, "On the Death of Cities," *The Public Interest* 45 (Fall 1976): 3-19.

6. Ibid.: 3-4.

7. For an example of convergence theories, see Jeffrey G. Williamson, "Regional Inequality and the Process of National Development," *Economic Development and Cultural Change* 13, 1 (1965): 3-45; and George Borts and Jerome L. Stein, *Economic Growth in a Free Market* (New York: Columbia Univ. Press, 1964).

8. For an empirical demonstration of convergence, see Simon Kuznets, Ann Miller, and Richard Easterlin, *Population Redistribution and Economic Growth: United States, 1870-1950* (Philadelphia: American Philosophical Society, 1960); Robert Crowley, "Reflections and Further Evidence on Population Size and Industrial Diversification," *Urban Studies* 10, 1 (1973): 91-94; Ben Chinitz and R. Dussansky, "The Patterns of Urbanization Within Regions of the U.S.," *Urban Studies* 9, 3 (1972): 289-298; and Frank Hannah, *State Income Differentials: 1919-1945* (Durham, NC: Duke Univ. Press, 1959).

9. Gunnar Myrdal, *Economic Theory and Underdeveloped Regions* (New York: Harper & Row, 1957): 13.

10. Adolph Lowe, *On Economic Knowledge* (New York: Harper & Row, 1965): 198-199.

Chapter 2

CLASSICAL LOCATION THEORY

Location theory analyzes the forces that regulate the spatial distribution of economic activities within an economy. It utilizes marginal analysis to determine the conditions that allow an entrepreneur to maximize revenues or minimize costs within a spatial context.

General equilibrium theory also enumerates the conditions associated with profit maximization, but according to Isard, it is limited to a situation "in which transport costs are taken as zero and outputs are viewed as perfectly mobile."[1] A more comprehensive and realistic approach, therefore, must account for the frictions imposed by distance. This can be accomplished by expanding the concept of factors of production—which traditionally have included only land, labor, capital, and entrepreneurship—and including transport inputs as a distinct factor. Isard defines a transport input as "the movement of a unit of weight over a unit of distance."[2] He calls the price of a transport input the "transport rate."

Some economists would argue that transport inputs are implicitly included in the traditional definition of factors of production, but Isard disagrees. General equilibrium analysis determines the marginal rate of substitution between labor and capital. Equilibrium occurs when the marginal rate of substitution equals the relative prices of these two factors. Unfortunately, when the costs of traversing space exceed zero, this simple approach no longer works. Instead of a simple two-dimensional problem, we face a more complex situation involving three explicit substitution possibilities:

(1) substitution between transport inputs and between various outlays and revenues associated with the use of any of several different commodities or combinations of commodities in the production process;
(2) substitution associated with the use of any of several sources of any one commodity;
(3) substitution associated with the various places to which a commodity can be transported.[3]

With this expanded theory of substitution, Isard demonstrates that traditional general equilibrium analysis can only guarantee that a local optimum has been attained. If transport inputs are ignored, there is no assurance that these will coincide with the global optimum. For example, if factor costs vary randomly from place to place, then a profit-maximizing firm should move away from the location associated with minimum transport outlays whenever the savings obtained at the low factor cost site exceed the additional transport costs. Conversely, a firm should move to an isolated, distant region if this new location allows it to serve a market which has been ignored by the other firms in the industry. In the first case, the firm obtains lower total costs by substituting higher transportation charges for lower factor costs. In the second example, the firm exchanges greater market control and a higher total revenue for lower transport costs. Treating the economy as if all production and marketing occur at a single point obscures these tradeoffs. But including transport inputs as a separate factor of production corrects this oversight and enhances the explanatory power of general equilibrium theory.

More importantly, since it focuses explicitly on the spatial arrangement of economic activity, location theory can illuminate the forces that attract and repel industry from urban areas and create variations in urban growth rates. A city with a favorable location will attract industry. A city with less desirable location attributes will see its industrial base dwindle.

But what exactly do we mean by the phrase "a favorable location"? In an attempt to answer this question, location theorists have developed two distinct paradigms focusing on different qualities that attract firms to a specific site.[4] Classical location theory, developed by such theorists as Von Thunen,[5] Weber,[6] and Hoover[7] , emphasizes the substitution possibilities that allow a firm to discover the least-cost location. In this approach, "Price is given and buyers are assumed to be concentrated at point formed consuming centers. The location decision, in reference to a given market center, rests solely upon cost, there being no sales advantage to be gained at the alternative locations which are tributary to the selected market."[8]

Four assumptions form the foundation of classical location theory:

(1) A production unit will only sell to one consuming center.
(2) The relevant consuming center can be represented by a point in space, i.e., markets are concentrated, not geographically dispersed.
(3) All firms operate in a perfectly competitive market environment and each must sell at the market-determined price irrespective of its costs of production.
(4) Variations in average cost are a function of the firm's location.

By adding the additional requirement that costs vary directly with distance from the least-cost location,[9] we can develop a simple geometrical illustration of the least-cost model of location theory (Figure 2.1). In this example, a profit-maximizing entrepreneur will locate at 0, the point where average cost is minimized. Any location within the interval AB will also be profitable although these alternatives are clearly suboptimal. Outside this interval, however, the firm operates at a loss. The least-cost model determines (a) those factors which cause spatial

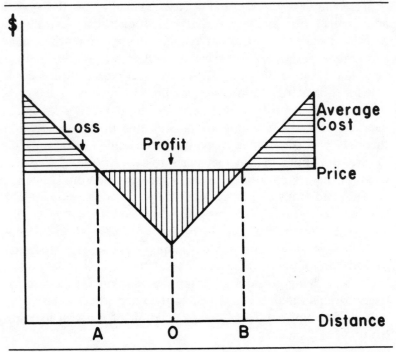

Figure 2.1: Least Cost Location Theory

variations in cost (transport rates, labor costs, and agglomeration economies), (b) the substitution possibilities between these
variables, and (c) the influence of these items on urban growth
and decay.

In contrast to classical location theory, market area analysis
gained more prominence as derivative of monopolistic competition theory than as a branch of location and urban theory.
Developed by such economists as Hotelling,[10] Fetter,[11] Lerner
and Singer,[12] Smithies,[13] and Chamberlain[14], it was predicated
upon the theory of duopoly. "It abstracted from cost and
explained the location of firms as the endeavor to control the
largest market areas. The methodology and conclusions were in
contrast with Weberian (least cost) findings."[15] Within the
context of market area analysis, a firm tries to maximize total

revenue while taking into consideration the elasticity of demand by consumers at different locations, the structure of transport rates, and the optimum amount of freight absorption or phantom freight. Various pricing strategies such as basing points and F.O.B. also come under the purview of market area analysis.

Several important distinctions between the two approaches should be explicitly noted. First, the goal of classical location theory is cost minimization. Market area analysis seeks revenue maximization. Second, with least-cost analysis, the price paid by the consumer remains constant while costs vary according to the producer's location. In market area analysis, costs do not vary with location, but the price paid by the consumer, which is calculated by summing factory costs and transportation charges, increases as distance from the production point increases. Third, with market area analysis, consumers are geographically dispersed. The size of a firm's market depends upon the geographic pattern of delivered prices. In the least-cost approach, consumers are all located at one point. Therefore, the extent of the firm's market does not depend upon the distance between the producer and the consumer. Rather, it is a function of the population at the consuming center and the ability of the firm to undersell its rivals. Finally, since each firm sells at a uniform, market-determined price, the least-cost approach assumes pure competition. Any firm can enter the market, and since all producers sell at the same price, consumers are indifferent as to which supplier they patronize. In market area analysis, location conveys an element of market control. By locating in a particular area, and by considering the location of both its rivals and customers, a firm can achieve a spatial monopoly. Market area analysis, therefore, tries to find the location which maximizes the firm's monopoly control.

These differences may be seen more clearly by comparing Figure 2.1 with Figure 2.2. In Figure 2.2, point 0 represents the location which yields the maximum profits. At any other site, the firm's revenues will be reduced by the competitive encroachment of better located rivals. Furthermore, if the firm does locate at 0, its market will extend, at most, from point A

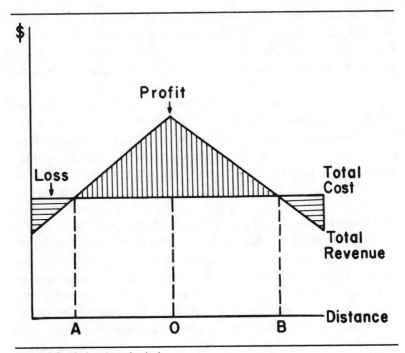

Figure 2.2: Market Area Analysis

to point B. Beyond this interval, it can be undersold by the other firms. But within the interval AB, the firm has monopoly control.

VON THUNEN

Von Thunen formulated the first systematic least-cost theory of industrial location. However, his approach differs in several major respects from all other location theorists. Rather than focusing on the factors that influence the location of a specific industry, Von Thunen first selected a location and then searched for the industry that would be most profitable at that site. After the most viable industry had been identified, Von Thunen studied the influence of location on capital intensity. He derived solutions to both problems by considering the impact of distance between the point of production and the point of consumption on transport costs, land rent, and cost of production. Since he assumed that the geographical pattern of costs was known before production commenced, an entrepreneur who had previously selected a location would then be able to determine which product, produced with what capital intensity, was best suited for that parcel of land.

At first this may appear to be an absurd approach. Generally, an entrepreneur will first select a business and then a location. But Von Thunen dealt with a preindustrial, agricultural economy in which land was inherited and the farmer had to choose among various crops in order to maximize his rent. Therefore, Von Thunen's theory is concerned primarily with the spatial determinants of rent. To the extent that rent is a function of what is produced on the land, the capital intensity of cultivation, and distance from the market center, his theory falls within the confines of location analysis.

Transport Costs and Rent

Von Thunen began his study of agricultural location by defining an isolated state composed of a "large town" and a vast rural hinterland "crossed by no navigable river or canal." The town supplies the hinterland with "all manufactured products" and obtains "all its provisions from the surrounding countryside." He then poses the following question: "What pattern of cultivation will take shape in these conditions and how will the farming system of the different districts be affected by their distance from the town?"[16] He replies to his rhetorical question by declaring:

It is on the whole obvious that near the town will be grown those products which are heavy or bulky in relation to their value and hence so expensive to transport that the remoter districts are unable to supply them. Here too we shall find the highly perishable products, which must be used very quickly. With increasing distance from the town, the land will progressively be given up to products cheap to transport in relation to their value. For this reason alone, fairly sharply differentiated concentric rings or belts will form around the town, each with its own particular staple product.[17]

In other words, in Von Thunen's approach, transport costs are paid by the producer and constitute a deduction from his rent. Figure 2.3 illustrates the influence of transport costs on rent and the evolution of the concentric rings. Let 0 represent the market for the agricultural produce. The rent that crop I yields when it is produced in the immediate vicinity of the market is OA. Similarly, OF is the rent derived from the production of crop II near the market. Thus, in the zone immediately adjacent to the city, crop I, which yields the highest rent, will be produced. But as the distance from the market increases, the relative profitability changes. If we assume that crop I is more expensive to transport, then with increasing distance from the market, the rent will decline more rapidly for crop I than for crop II. Consequently, within the XY zone, crop I will be produced while outside these boundaries, cultivation will shift to crop II. If we extend the analysis to more than two crops, a series of concentric rings or zones will emerge. Within each ring one crop will be the most profitable. The zone nearest the market will be used to cultivate that crop which faces the greatest cost increase away from the market. The outer zones will produce those products that have the lowest transport rate.

To understand the dynamic implications of Von Thunen's theory, the analysis must include several other variables besides transport costs. According to Losch,[18] a more sophisticated analysis of ring formation can be derived from the following equation:

$$R = E(p-a) - Efk, \text{ where}$$

R = rent per unit of land
K = distance
E = yield per unit of land
p = market price per unit of commodity
a = production cost per unit of commodity
f = transport rate per unit of distance for each commodity

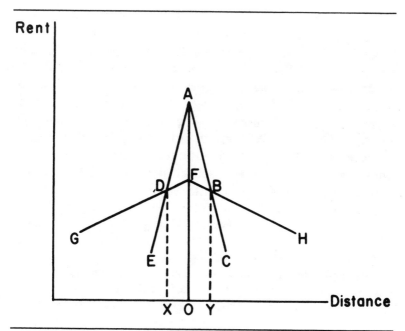

Figure 2.3: Von Thunen's Theory of Concentric Rings

Rent will be zero when p–a = fK or, in other words, when transport costs absorb the profits obtained by cultivating a particular crop. The maximum distance at which a cash crop will be produced can be determined if we assume that production for the market will continue until rents are reduced to zero. Then, the maximum distance from the city consistent with a nonsubsistence form of agriculture can be expressed as $K = \frac{p-a}{f}$. If p and a are treated as constants, then production of cash crops will expand as freight rates fall because "agricultural production becomes profitable over a more extended area. . . . Under the influence of a progressive improvement in transport technology the zones of production will tend to move outward from the central markets."[19]

This hypothesis can be tested by examining the influence of the "world metropolis"[20] on the zones of agricultural produc-

tion in the United States. In this test, however, we will not limit
the analysis to the changing pattern of production found in the
vicinity of a single urban center. Although Von Thunen's analysis assumes that "as far as commercial farming is concerned, the
countryside is and always has been an economic dependency of
the metropolis,"[21] the concept of "the countryside" must be
expanded to include more than the farming areas immediately
adjacent to a city. Not every city has a hinterland which
produces the full range of agricultural products. Therefore, Von
Thunen's assumption of an "isolated state" must be regarded as
a mere methodological convenience.

A more realistic description of ring behavior within the
context of an interrelated system of cities is provided by Losch
who writes:

> The rings under discussion form around each new center, but in a
> region of many towns there is no room for the outer ones; they are
> displaced toward its margins. The number of displaced rings in-
> creases with the density of towns. For the inner rings the individual
> town is the marketing center, for the outer ones the agglomeration
> of towns.[22]

Thus, as transportation facilities improve and reduce the cost
of shipping agricultural commodities, we should discover that
those crops that would have been relegated to the outer rings
under the assumption of an "isolated state" will move further
from the area of dense urban settlement. In addition, regions
that had previously been engaged in subsistence farming should
find themselves drawn into the web of commercial agriculture.
The isolation of the frontier therefore, should not be attributed
to soil fertility or other natural conditions which might inhibit
cultivation. It occurs only "because means of transport [are]
lacking rather than because of a non-market orientation. . . . In
America, subsistence was only a frontier condition to be overcome as rapidly as means of transportation could be built
up."[23]

In the frontier regions of the United States, the high freight
rates preceding the vast program of internal improvements mil-

itated against commercial agriculture. In 1816, before the construction of the Erie Canal, the cost of transporting one ton of goods from Europe to New York was $9.00. This same nine dollars would have paid for the transportation of one ton of freight 30 miles over the primitive turnpike system then in existence.[24] Neither high-value manufactured goods nor low-value, bulky farm produce could be sold at a profit under the prevailing system of freight rates.

With the construction of canals and railroads, freight rates plummeted. In 1817 it cost 19.12 cents per ton mile to ship goods from Buffalo to New York. By 1830, only five years after the completion of the Erie Canal, the freight charge was 1.68 cents per ton mile, and by 1857, after further improvements were completed, the price had fallen to .8155 cents per ton mile. In only forty years, the rate dropped by 95%. Turnpike rates also dropped, although not as dramatically. Previously, wagon-hauling charges ranged from 30 to 70 cents per ton mile. By 1824 they were only 13 cents per ton mile—a rate that prevailed through 1860.[25]

As a result of these freight rate reductions, agricultural produce from the Midwest began to pour into the cities along the East Coast. According to one expert who studied commodity shipments through the Erie Canal, this reduction in freight rates had a major influence on the development of commercial agriculture in the Midwest:

> For the first time the bulky products of the West began to flow directly eastward. By connecting with the Great Lakes, the canal system of New York had tapped the finest inland waterway in the world. The immigrants who crowded the Erie canalboats and settled first in Ohio, Indiana, and Michigan, and later in the more western lake states, soon sent back over the route they had travelled an increasing flow of flour, wheat, and other frontier products. By 1835, flour and wheat, equal to 268,000 barrels of flour, were shipped from the West to tidewater via the Erie; by 1840, shipments exceeded 1,000,000 barrels. By 1860 they totalled 4,344,000 barrels. . . . After 1848 Buffalo received wheat and flour even from faraway St. Louis via the Illinois River, the Illinois and Michigan Canal, and the Lakes.[26]

The development of railroads further extended the zone of commercial agriculture and shortened the period between the initial settlement of an area and its absorption into the commercial network. In some instances, railroads were in direct competition with canals, but in their early days, they generally served as a feeder system collecting produce from the more remote land-locked areas and delivering it to a point where it could be transferred to canal boats for the remainder of the journey. Where railroads and canals traversed parallel routes, the competition between the two modes reduced transport charges even further.

As a result of these cost reductions, the zone of extensive agriculture moved from the urbanized Northeast to the more remote areas in the West Central United States. In 1800, for instance, the middle Atlantic states exported both wheat and livestock to New England, the Carolinas, and the West Indies.[27] But as Table 2.1 indicates, by 1859 the leading wheat-growing region had shifted to the Midwest and by 1899 to the Dakotas, Kansas, and Minnesota.[28] With the growth of urban centers and the development of internal improvements, the effective proximity of a parcel of land to the "world metropolis" increased. Because of this increased proximity, it was not uncommon to find that "on a single farm, a man might in his own lifetime be in cattle country, wheat country, corn country, and dairy country."[29] Cultivation, in other words, shifted from extensive to intensive as the city's influence expanded into the frontier.

While these developments pushed the extensive zones deeper into the continent, they also affected production on land adjacent to the urban centers. Land that had previously been used for extensive farming shifted to intensive cultivation or was removed from agricultural production altogether. In 1838, one Massachusetts observer wrote:

The times are changed and we must change with them. We cannot now, as formerly, raise much grain for the market. The virgin soils of the West and the increasing facilities of intercourse with that region

TABLE 2.1 The Six Leading Wheat States by Decades, 1859–1899

1859	1869	1879	1889	1899
Illinois	Illinois	Illinois	Minnesota	Minnesota
Indiana	Iowa	Indiana	California	North Dakota
Wisconsin	Ohio	Ohio	Illinois	Ohio
Ohio	Indiana	Michigan	Indiana	South Dakota
Virginia	Wisconsin	Minnesota	Ohio	Kansas
Pennsylvania	Pennsylvania	Iowa	Kansas	California

SOURCE: Fred A. Shannon, *The Farmer's Last Frontier* (New York: Farrar Rinehart, 1945): 163.

render it probable that much of our grain will be imported thence; and when no obstacles are thrown in the way of commerce, this is no evil. We purchase, not because we cannot produce the same commodity, but because we can produce others to more profit. Let them supply our cities with grain. We will manufacture their cloth and their shoes.[30]

This brief historical excursion suggests that when farmers decide what crop to cultivate, they must consider two factors—the rent they can afford to pay and the rent they are forced to pay.[31] The latter falls rapidly as distance from the urban center increases. The former is jointly determined by the price the produce commands at the market and transportation charges. As distance from the city increases, freight charges absorb the residual between total revenue and nontransport costs. This residual, the rent a farmer can afford to pay, also decreases as cultivation shifts to more remote areas but since it declines more slowly than the rent he is forced to pay, relocating the extensive branches of farming to the outer zones eventually brings the two back into equilibrium.

However, as the "world metropolis" grows, land in formerly remote areas increases in value and this destroys the previous equilibrium. By crowding out those crops which cannot afford the higher land costs, it forces farmers to relocate further from the city. If transportation improvements do not materialize, then one of two possible events will occur. Food prices may rise and this will permit food and raw materials to be transported over greater distances. However, if food prices do not rise, then the lack of cheap transportation facilities will prematurely stifle urban growth. But the development of cheap transportation facilities precludes both higher food prices and truncated urban development. Extensive forms of cultivation can now shift to the more distant zones without endangering the cheap supply of food and raw materials that are needed to attract industry and support a large urban population.

Thus, if we use Von Thunen's approach to analyze the dynamic forces producing zonal shifts in agriculture, the feverish canal and railroad development assumes additional urgency. These activities were both a cause and a prerequisite of rapid urbanization. During the mercantile era, those cities that extended their hinterlands and brought new agricultural areas within their orbits were the most prosperous. At that time, mercantile functions were the dynamic, city-building activity. But without the completion of these tasks, not only would individual cities have experienced slower growth but the expansion of the entire system of cities would have been seriously constrained. To this extent, mercantile functions were both city building and system building.

Distance and Capital Intensity

The zonal arrangement of agriculture and the influence of cities on the width of these zones comprise only one half of Von Thunen's theory. The interaction between distance, urbanization, and capital intensity is an equally important component of his work.

According to Von Thunen, a farmer's costs can be disaggregated into two elements—farm-based costs (wages, seeds, manure, etc.), which provide the means of subsistence and are expressed in terms of bushels of grain although they must eventually be paid in cash, and city-based costs, which represent the monetary outlays for the agricultural implements produced in urban workshops.[32] Because the price of grain at the point of production equals the price of grain in the city minus transportation charges, farm-based costs and grain prices are inversely related to distance from the urban center. But since only farm-based costs fall with falling grain prices while city-based costs remain constant, as cultivation spreads into more distant regions, total costs fall more slowly than grain prices. Therefore, beyond a certain distance, the extra monetary return from more intensive methods will not offset the additional costs of production. Conversely, as one approaches the city, the price of agricultural products rises, but the expenses of the farm do not increase as rapidly. Therefore, regions near the city can afford to employ capital-intensive techniques.

In terms of Losch's rent formula, we can demonstrate that "intensification brings a higher rent; but as compared with the less intensive methods, it stops being profitable at smaller distances from the market."[33] At locations near the market, the transport burden (- fK) is low, but it increases in direct proportion to distance. Gross returns (p- a) are higher near the market but decrease more rapidly than the transport burden due to the functional relationship between costs, prices, and distance. Since the net return or rent (which is equal to gross returns minus the transport burden) is highest in the vicinity of the city, a profit-maximizing farmer can increase his profits by introducing intensive cultivation and increasing his yield per acre (E). In more distant locations, profits will be maximized by reducing the transport burden (hauling fewer goods over a given distance) and by reducing costs as rapidly as possible (economizing on city-based costs). This implies lower yields per acre and a smaller dose of capital. In other words, by equating marginal costs and marginal revenue, which are both functionally related to distance, farmers can achieve the spatial arrangement of intensity consistent with maximum profits.

Figure 2.4 presents a diagrammatic illustration of the relationship between urbanization and capital intensity.[34] In this diagram, the horizontal axis measures capital intensity, and the

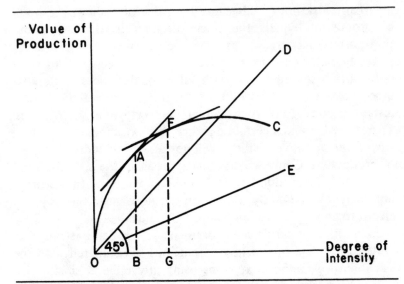

Figure 2.4: Von Thunen's Theory of Capital Intensity

vertical axis measures the value of production. Because of
diminishing returns, the value of production rises more slowly
than capital intensity, producing a total product curve that is
convex from above. If we assume that the costs of production
are directly proportional to capital intensity, then the distance
between the 45° line (OD) and the total product curve equals
the farmer's rent or net return. This will be maximized when
the tangent to the total product curve is parallel to the 45° line.
From the diagram, we see that OB is the optimal capital
intensity consistent with profit maximization.

However, with the rise of cities in previously nonurbanized
regions, the cost of transporting the product to the market
decreases because of the shorter distance that must be traversed
and the cheaper transport rates that historically have accompanied the growth of cities. Diagrammatically, this can be
represented by drawing a new ray through the origin with a
slope of less than 45° (OE). This increases the capital intensity
of agriculture from OB to OG.

Although the extensive literature dealing with the mechanization of agriculture will not be reviewed here,[35] the influence of urban development on agricultural mechanization in the United States can be tested by observing the recent changes in the amount of capital devoted to agriculture. If Von Thunen's theory is correct, those states that were heavily urbanized in the beginning of the period should also contain the most mechanized farms. Those states that were devoid of major urban centers should have less mechanized farms. However, as urban growth occurs in the previously nonurbanized states, these disparities should decrease. Although it would be a gross over-simplification to attribute all these changes solely to the rise of urban areas, as Table 2.2 indicates, the general pattern predicted by Von Thunen has been followed. In 1940, the average value of machinery and equipment per farm in six southern states was approximately 40% of the value in six heavily urbanized states. By 1969, this value had increased to 90%.

Contemporary Applications

Despite its preindustrial, agricultural orientation, Von Thunen's theoretical insights have been borrowed by contemporary scholars to explain the intrametropolitan location of economic activity.[36] Studies of urban rent gradients[37] indicate that the price of land and the rent that a particular parcel commands fall as distance from the central business district increases. Metropolitan rent variations, therefore, follow the pattern suggested by Von Thunen. If we can determine the impact of changing transportation technologies on intrametropolitan transportation costs and the effect of technological innovations on capital intensity, then, Von Thunen's analysis can explain the relocation of certain industries into the more remote districts of the metropolitan area.[38] If the process of geographical diffusion propels industry beyond the arbitrary, political boundaries of the incorporated municipality, then Von Thunen's approach can account for some of the forces producing suburbanization of industry.

TABLE 2.2   Average Market Value of Machinery and Equipment per
Farm by State, 1940 and 1969

State	1940	1969	State	1940	1969
Massachusetts	521	8,458	North Carolina	163	5,227
New York	903	12,324	South Carolina	176	6,615
Pennsylvania	764	9,675	Florida	327	8,366
Ohio	514	8,312	Louisiana	239	10,164
Wisconsin	931	10,572	Texas	432	7,695
Minnesota	980	12,162	Arizona	539	16,354
Average	768	10,250	Average	312	9,070

SOURCES: For 1940 figures – U.S. Department of Commerce, 16th Census of the
United States, *Agriculture*, Volume III, General Report, Table 16. For 1969 figures
– 1969 Census of Agriculture, Chapter 4, *Equipment, Labor Expenditures, and
Chemicals*, Table 15.

The tradeoff between transportation costs and rent, which
forms the core of Von Thunen's analysis, can also explain the
pattern and dynamics of residential land use. Those individuals
demanding space extensive housing facilities will, according to
the theory, locate in the outer rings where rent per acre is
lowest. By moving to this location, they substitute higher transportation costs for lower land costs. Conversely, those individuals who desire a more proximate residential site will substitute higher land costs for lower transportation charges. Moreover, with the advent of cheap intraurban commuting facilities,
the outer zones of residential settlement will be extended and
those exurbanites who previously had little daily contact with
the city will find that their "frontier" isolation has been terminated.[39] Thus, there is a symmetry between the dynamics of
agricultural land use and urban residential land use.

TRANSPORT COSTS

Classical location theory ignores the functional relationship
between rent and distance from an urban center. Instead, it
emphasizes the impact of transport costs on industrial location.
Such theorists as Weber, Hoover, and Losch first determine the

location that minimizes a firm's total transport costs. After this point has been identified, they consider spatial variations in processing costs and the substitution possibilities between transfer costs and processing costs. Consequently, any attempt to fuse location theory with urban growth must consider the relationship between transport costs and industrial location.

Location Near Raw Materials

If a manufacturing process utilizes bulky materials that lose weight during their conversion into a finished product, and if the cost of transporting the raw material is greater than the cost of transporting the finished product, then the least-cost location will be at the raw material site. Transport costs will be minimized by locating near the raw material requiring the greatest transport outlay. Firms with this location preference are "material oriented."

Especially during the early periods of American economic development, material-oriented production processes played a decisive role in the growth and decline of cities. For example, the fuel used in blast furnaces was the most important factor governing the location of steel mills.[40] When wood was the primary fuel, the industry located near forests, and steel production was a rural industry. However, with the introduction of coal, the industry centralized in western Pennsylvania and eastern Ohio. By locating at the fuel source, steel producers minimized the transportation of a bulky, weight-losing input and those cities situated in the vicinity of coal deposits soon became the leading steel centers in the United States. In 1900, for example, Pittsburgh produced 11.3% of the nation's steel.[41] Other major steel cities in 1900 were McKeesport, Youngstown, Cleveland, Johnstown, and Newcastle. Only two states, Pennsylvania and Ohio, produced 71.3% of the nation's steel output. Moreover, steel production was the major industry in each of these cities. In McKeesport, steel production comprised 92.6% of the city's industrial production. Pittsburgh, the most diversified of the steel centers in 1900, had 44.7% of its industrial output originate in the steel sector. Thus, the fortunes of these cities were directly tied to the forces determining the location of steel production.

Meat packing and slaughtering began as a market-oriented industry, but forces associated with urban growth, transportation improvements, and technological change caused it to adopt a material orientation. Because of this shift in its location propensity, meat packing became centralized in a few advantageously located metropolitan areas, and those cities capturing a major portion of this qualitatively new industry rose rapidly in the urban hierarchy.

In its early years, the lack of refrigeration forced meat packers to locate near the major consuming centers. To provide fresh meat, the cattle and hogs literally had to walk to the markets where they were then butchered and consumed. However, the inability of live animals to traverse long distances and the cost associated with cattle drives limited the city's supply area.

At this point, the railroads stepped in and provided a more efficient method of transporting cattle to market. Since the grazing areas had been displaced to the outer zones of the "world metropolis," cattle drives terminated at rail depots, and the rest of the journey was conducted by rail. Abilene, Kansas, served as the first rail terminus for cattle drives. However, the spread of wheat cultivation into eastern Kansas ended Abilene's supremacy and rapid growth. When the farmers near Abilene saw their crops continuously trampled by cattle herds, they forced the railroad to stop transporting live animals. Wichita, Kansas, which was west of the settled and cultivated area, emerged as the new depot. "On June 8, 1872, eighteen carloads of cattle were shipped out for Chicago and before the end of the year, a total of 3,530 carloads, or nearly 350,000 steers. Wichita's career as a cowtown was launched. Abilene shrank into insignificance."[42] At this stage in the evolution of the meat packing and slaughtering industry, the actual butchering was still market oriented but the transportation of cattle had developed into a material-oriented, city-building activity.

The invention of refrigeration cars led to the final transformation of the meat packing and slaughtering industry. Since shipping live animals cost more than transporting processed meat, only the slaughtered carcass was shipped. Those midwestern cities with adequate rail facilities soon emerged as the meat packing centers in the United States. In 1890, for example, 44.9% of all meat packing was centralized in Chicago, although by 1900 this figure dropped to 35.6%. Kansas City, Kansas, with 10.5% of the nation's meat packing activity and South Omaha with 9.7% were the other leading centers. Buffalo, Cincinatti, Cleveland, Milwaukee, Baltimore, Philadelphia, and New York City, which formerly had been major meat packing centers because of their large populations, became minor centers. By 1900, none had more than 1.8% of the national meat packing activity located within their borders.[43]

However, not only did the least-cost location shift, but as a result of its new orientation, the entire meat packing industry was qualitatively transformed. When every city had its own meat packing facilities, the prosperity of the local economy did not depend on meat packing and the loss of this activity due to its new orientation was a minor event. Its reappearance in a few Midwestern cities, however, had profound significance. Meat packing had been converted into an activity that could influence the prosperity of an entire city. For example, by 1900, the meat packing industry in Baltimore, Philadelphia, and New York accounted for less than 1% of the local value added. In South Omaha, Nebraska, meat packing constituted 96.3% of the value of all manufactured products. In Kansas City meat packing constituted 88.4% and in Chicago 28.0%. For these three cities, the fate of the meat packing industry and the fate of the city were inseparable. In Baltimore, Philadelphia, and New York, the fate of the meat packing industry had little or no impact on local prosperity.

Transport Costs and Market Orientation

Although material oriented processes influenced the growth and prosperity of some urban centers, other cities were notably deficient in material processing industries. "The paucity of raw materials goes some way toward explaining their absence."[44]

As a result, the industrial base in these cities must be attributed to a different locational advantage.

If "the final product is more expensive to transport than the raw material, the finished good is perishable, the consumer demand is capricious and volatile or close contact with the consumer enhances sales,"[45] then the manufacturing process is market oriented. These producers will locate in the region with greatest market potential in order to minimize the distribution cost of supplying the market. Their location decision will be relatively less influenced by the location of raw materials.

Recent evidence indicates that market potential or market orientation has become increasingly more important in plant location decisions. Several factors account for this phenomenon. First, as products become more technologically sophisticated, the initial processing of raw materials contributes a smaller portion of the total value added. This weakens the manufacturers' attraction to the raw material site. Second, technological changes have increased the efficiency of raw material processing. For example, Isard reports that in the middle of the nineteenth century, one ton of pig iron required eight tons of coal and three tons of iron ore.[46] By 1952, these figures declined to 1.2 tons of iron ore and .9 tons of coal. In addition, each ton of steel new utilizes .6 tons of scrap metal, found primarily in the market areas of the U.S.[47] Because of these changes, raw materials now exert less influence on a firm's location.

The changing structure of transport rates has also contributed to the market orientation of manufacturing. For example, Chinitz reports that unlike the nineteenth century, transportation charges have been rising more rapidly than processing costs. Consequently, manufacturers now have a greater incentive to minimize transportation charges. When coupled with the fact that freight rates on raw materials have risen less than freight charges on finished products, the incentive to locate near the raw material site diminishes greatly. Instead, a location near the market will produce the greatest savings.[48]

These tendencies have been intensified by the rate differentials between long hauls and short hauls. Transport charges contain two components—terminal costs and line haul costs. Terminal charges are analogous to fixed costs. If they can be spread over more units, their impact on average total cost will be reduced. Line haul costs, on the other hand, vary directly with distance. With a given terminal cost, the transport rate (terminal charges plus line haul costs) per ton of material will not rise very rapidly if the product is shipped long distance. Under these circumstances, the discovery of raw material deposits in remote areas will not induce manufacturers who use the materials to relocate near their source.

Yet the same reasoning should also persuade market-oriented manufacturers to relocate away from their market so that they too can take advantage of the relatively low long-haul rates. Why have they remained in the vicinity of the market and agreed to pay the relatively more expensive short-haul rates? Figure 2.5 provides the answer to this question. Technological changes in transportation created new freight modes that require lower terminal charges. (In Figure 2.5 terminal charges are represented by the y intercept.) Moreover, these new transport modes are more appropriate for finished products, not bulky raw materials. As a result of these technological advances, short-haul rates for finished products have fallen faster than long-haul rates for raw materials. In other words, by switching from railroads to trucks, shippers of finished products have converted to the mode that is most economical for short hauls. This development favors market-oriented processes.

Finally, the freight differential between components and finished products also favors a market orientation. Because finished assembled products are often bulkier and require more delicate handling, they carry heavier freight charges. Conversely, components are more compact and cheaper to ship. Therefore, as the number of components contained in a finished product increases, the savings obtained by shipping the parts to an assembly plant located near the market also increase. Thus,

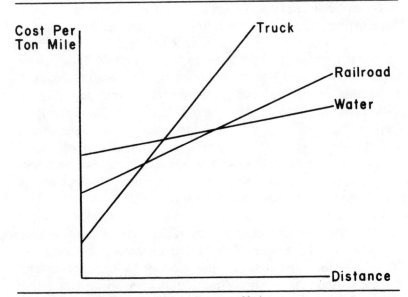

Figure 2.5: Total Cost per Ton Mile by Transport Mode

although intermediate goods producers may be somewhat footloose, producers of final products are more market oriented.[49]

All of these trends suggest that a market orientation is becoming more economical than a material orientation. To test this hypothesis, we can investigate whether regions with high market potential gain manufacturing jobs at a faster rate than regions with low market potential.

In a 1954 study, Harris notes that the highest market potential in the United States extends along a straight line from New York City to Chicago.[50] Two other studies concerned with the geographical distribution of manufacturing growth conclude that between 1919 and 1947, the greatest manufacturing growth occurred precisely in the region that Harris identified.[51] Moreover, the cities within this high market potential zone were among the fastest growing in the nation. During this period, such cities as Detroit, Cincinnati, Toledo, Akron, and Youngstown capitalized on their favorable location and emerged as major manufacturing centers.

TABLE 2.3   Regional Share of National Population and National Production Employees in the Manufacturing Sector

Region	Share of 1950 Population	Share of 1970 Population	Share of 1947 Manufacturing Production Workers	Share of 1972 Manufacturing Production Workers
New England	6.2	5.8	10.5	6.6
Middle Atlantic	19.9	18.2	27.2	19.2
East-North Central	20.1	19.7	29.9	25.1
West-North Central	9.3	8.0	5.3	5.9
South Atlantic	13.9	15.0	11.3	15.5
East-South Central	7.6	6.2	4.7	7.4
West-South Central	9.6	9.4	3.8	6.6
Mountain	3.3	4.0	1.0	2.2
Pacific	9.6	13.0	6.3	9.6

SOURCES: 1947 and 1950 data were obtained from Coleman Woodbury and Frank Cliffe, "Industrial Location and Urban Redevelopment" in Coleman Woodbury (ed.), *The Future of Cities and Urban Redevelopment* (Chicago: Univ. of Chicago Press, 1953): 148-149; 1970 and 1972 data were obtained from U.S. Department of Commerce, *1972 City County Data Book* (Washington DC: U.S. Government Printing Office, 1974).

However, since 1947, migration flows have been directed toward the Sunbelt, not the industrial Northeast.[52] By increasing the market potential of the Sunbelt, these population flows should also induce rapid manufacturing employment growth in this region. The data in Table 2.3 provide a rough confirmation of this hypothesis and suggest that market potential remains a powerful inducement for manufacturers. With the exception of the west north central and east south central census divisions, the relative share of national population and the relative share of manufacturing production workers moved in the same direction.

The Location of Cities

Up to this point, we have used location theory to identify two locational preferences—the source of the raw materials and the final market. In addition, we have shown how various cities prospered as a result of their fortuitous location. Those cities that were advantageously situated became the center of a particular industry and moved rapidly up the ranks of the urban hierarchy. Those cities that were unable to maintain their location advantage either failed to grow or declined in importance. Thus, even though the principles of location theory do not deal specifically with the process of urban growth and uneven development, they can be adopted to explain the rise and fall of certain urban areas.

For example, location theory can account for the rise of cities at transhipment points.[53] The economies associated with a location at a transhipment or break in bulk point are illustrated in Figure 2.6. Assume that the raw materials site is at M and the final market is at C. Separating both sites is a barrier, B, which prevents the uninterrupted transportation of both raw materials and the finished product. Panel A and panel B demonstrate the locational preferences of a firm that does not have to contend with a transportation barrier. In panel A, assembly costs exceed distribution costs, so the firm will be material oriented. The situation for a market-oriented firm is shown in panel B. In both cases, an intermediate location would be suboptimal since cities located at an end point will have a cost advantage. Panel C assumes equal transport costs for raw materials and the finished product. Without a transportation barrier, firms will be indifferent—they will experience no disadvantage by locating at either end point or at some intermediate point. The existence of a barrier, however, eliminates this indifference. Now the firm's only viable location will be at B. If the firm locates at C, then assembly costs will be a+b+c, where b signifies the cost of surmounting the barrier. Similarly, by locating at M, the total distribution costs will be d+b+e. However, if the firm chooses site B, then both the assembly costs and the distribution costs will be reduced by b since neither the raw materials nor the finished product will incur the cost of traversing the barrier. This is clearly the least-cost production site, and throughout history it has been one of the more viable locations for cities. Those cities situated at a transhipment point often grew rapidly. Those not so fortunate either declined or erected an artificial barrier to ensure their continued viability.

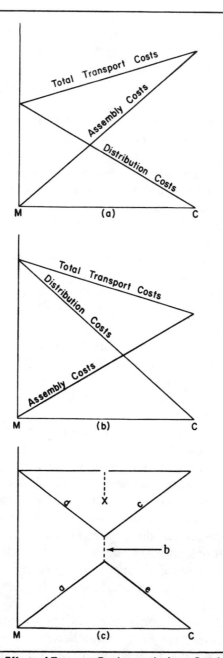

Figure 2.6: The Effects of Transport Barriers on the Least Cost Location

Early settlements in the United States were generally located at transhipment points. Boston, New York, Philadelphia, Charleston, New Orleans, Newport, Fairfield, New Haven, Wilmington, Norfolk, and Savannah among others were port cities that served as an "economic hinge" connecting the continental interior with Europe.[54] Goods passing in either direction had to be loaded or unloaded at their wharves. If processing was required then the transhipment point represented the logical location for this activity. Port cities, therefore, often developed manufacturing in conjunction with their mercantile functions although at least in the early stages of their growth, the manufacturing functions were subordinate to the more city-building mercantile activities.[55]

Ocean ports, however, do not provide the only natural transhipment points. River junctions are another excellent site.[56] Pittsburgh, for instance, is located at the confluence of the Monangahela, Allegheny, and Ohio Rivers. St. Louis is located on the west bank of the Mississippi, just south of the junction of the Missouri, Ohio, and Mississippi Rivers. Louisville, although only served by the Ohio River, is situated at a waterfall that imperiled shipping. All freight had to be unloaded, transported by land around the falls, and then reloaded on boats for the remainder of the journey. Minneapolis is another city situated in the vicinity of a waterfall.[57]

These sites provided natural locations for mercantile and material processing manufacturing activities. Commodities arriving from many directions would be shipped to these junction points where they were unloaded and consolidated with other cargoes headed for the same destination. These *entrepot* centers flourished due to the presence of such city-building, mercantile activities as freight handling, freight agencies, commercial financing operations, insurance agencies, and warehousing. With so many goods passing through these centers, it was only natural that material processing would also develop at the transhipment point.

Finally railroads and canals provided opportunities for creating transhipment centers. Buffalo, Rochester, and Albany developed rapidly after the completion of the Erie Canal. Buffalo and Rochester were located at the junction of the Great Lakes and the canal while Albany was situated at the canal's eastern terminus where goods were transferred from canal boats to larger vessels for the voyage down the Hudson River. Detroit, Chicago, Milwaukee, and Cleveland also prospered as a result of the Erie Canal. Previously, farm produce was shipped down river to New Orleans, the transhipment point between the Mississippi River and the Gulf of Mexico. By extending railroads and canals into their hinterlands, these Great Lakes port cities diverted commerce to the Erie Canal. They prospered because of their status as transhipment points between their canal and rail systems and the Great Lakes.[58]

In many instances, urban rivalries developed when two cities vied to create transhipment points serving the same region. Baltimore's attempt to provide a direct rail link via the Baltimore & Ohio Railroad to Wheeling, West Virginia, threatened Pittsburgh's supremacy as the dominant city at the head of the Ohio River as well as Philadelphia's control of trade originating in western Pennsylvania. Both Pennsylvania cities therefore pooled their resources to construct the Main Line linking Pittsburgh with Philadelphia. By this device, they hoped to thwart Baltimore's attempt to create a western transhipment point.[59]

Chicago businessmen constructed an extensive railroad system with the aim of replacing St. Louis as the dominant transhipment point in the midwest. Their efforts were a success.[60] The businessmen of Louisville and Cincinnati ended their rivalry by agreeing to a compromise that represented the height of inefficiency, but which ensured that both cities would retain their role as transhipment points. The fight began when a group of Cincinnati businessmen petitioned the Kentucky legislature for permission to construct a railroad through Kentucky. Louisville's businessmen, fearing that the proposed railroad would divert trade from their city, managed to delay the franchise for several years. The squabbling finally ended when the mercantile interests of both cities agreed that the railroad would pass through Louisville. However, the section between Louisville and Cincinnati would have a guage of 4'8-1/2" while the other portions would be constructed with 5' guage track. Since all freight would have to be unloaded and reloaded at each city, neither would automatically lose its status as a transhipment center.[61]

However, a location at a transhipment point does not necessarily ensure prosperity. New York City was both helped and hindered by its location. Both with respect to European trade and hinterland trade conducted via canals, New York's location provided a great advantage. But the development of the railroads reduced its superiority. Due to the barrier formed by the Hudson River, no direct rail link could be maintained between New York and the manufacturing belt. Manufacturers in Manhattan who wished to ship their goods west were forced to first float them by barge across the Hudson River where they would then be transferred to railroads. This required two additional terminal charges and effectively discouraged freight-sensitive operations from locating in New York.[62]

San Diego's potential as a transhipment point linking the Pacific Ocean and the Southern Pacific Railroad hampered its early growth and allowed Los Angeles to emerge as the dominant city in Southern California. San Francisco merchants, fearing that a transcontinental railroad terminating in San Diego would divert cargo from San Francisco, lobbied vigorously to reroute the railroad. They favored placing the western terminus in Los Angeles because it had "an inadequate and unprotected port."[63] Consequently, the railroad stopped in Los Angeles. San Diego, despite its more advantageous location, was soon overshadowed by its poorly endowed neighbor to the north.

AGGLOMERATION ECONOMIES
AND INDUSTRIAL CONCENTRATION

The preceding analysis assumes that processing costs do not vary with location. By modifying this assumption and considering interregional cost of production differentials we can highlight additional factors that promote uneven urban development. More specifically, location theorists suggest that cost of production disparities will induce firms to move from the site that minimizes total transport outlays if the savings in processing costs at the new site offset the added expense of assembling the raw materials and distributing the final product. Included in this list of variables that affect processing costs are such items as agglomeration economies, labor costs, tax burdens, and government subsidies. However, not every item in this list has the same impact on industrial location. Some produce centrifugal tendencies or industrial concentration. Others create centripetal tendencies or industrial dispersion.

Agglomeration economies lower processing costs when several firms or industries congregate in one region. Hoover lists three distinct cost-reducing mechanisms that fall under the heading of agglomeration economies:

(a) *large-scale economies* within a firm consequent upon the enlargement of the firm's scale of production at one point;

(b) *localization economies* for all the firms in a single industry at a single location, consequent upon the enlargement of the total output at that location; and

(c) *urbanization economies* for all firms in all industries at a single location, consequent upon the enlargement of the total economic size (population, income, output, or wealth) of that location, for all industries taken together.[64]

Large-Scale Economies

For certain industrial processes, the cost per unit of output decreases as the volume of output increases. Because of this relationship, large-scale economies or increasing returns to scale, induce concentration in a few production centers. For example, when numerous small producers are scattered throughout the region, the extent of each firm's market is too small to allow any one firm to capture the lower processing costs associated with large-scale production. However, by limiting production to a few locations, each of the surviving firms will produce a larger output at a lower average cost. Those cities with the best location or most perspicacious entrepreneurs will emerge as the production centers for that commodity.

Figure 2.7 illustrates the "city-building" influence associated with large scale economies. In panel A, economies of scale are not present. The producer located at A incurs processing costs totaling AC while the processing costs for the firm at site B equal BF. CDE and FDG represent the delivered prices for each production center.[65] Since consumers will patronize the firm that offers the lowest delivered price, both firms share the market and production continues at both sites.

In panel B, producer A realizes that by expanding output he can reduce his average cost and eliminate his rival. Although the transport costs incurred by supplying the distant consumers have increased, these additional outlays are more than offset by the lower processing costs. As a result, city A will prosper while city B declines.

Panel B assumes that only one firm recognizes the benefits associated with large-scale production. As a result, production concentrates in city A while city B disappears as a rival production site. Panel C depicts a more realistic scenario. Now, producers at both locations attempt to expand their market and gain the advantage of large scale production. Since concentration is equally feasible at both locations, the solution becomes indeterminate. Each firm will try to expand, but if they both attempt to enlarge their output, they will both face the constraint imposed by a limited market. The resolution of this impasse depends upon timing and initial advantage. "The location at which production is undertaken first is the location at which production is more likely to concentrate."[66]

Unfortunately, this response fails to explain which city will attract the large-scale output. Simply relying upon the concept of "initial advantage" is insufficient. We must ask, why has one city seized the opportunity before the other?

To answer this question, Alchian distinguishes between adaptive and adoptive behavior.[67] According to his analysis, success does not only accrue to the businessman who first obtains an accurate assessment of a particular situation and then adapts his behavior to the conditions he has observed. Those businessmen who pursue the correct course of action, even though motivated by ignorance, can also be successful. If their actions conform to

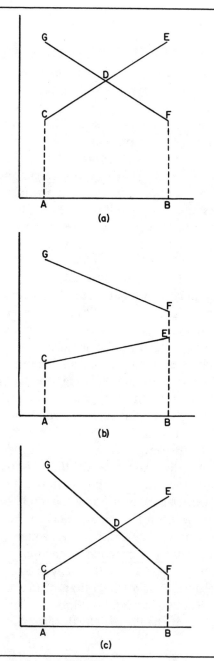

Figure 2.7: Economies of Scale and Industrial Concentration

the dictates of the market, they will be adopted by the economy.

Urban history is filled with examples of both types of behavior. Detroit, for instance, provides an excellent example of an adopted city. Many other cities would have been equally good locations for the automobile industry and although Detroit "had no grave disadvantages of situation to overcome, neither had she any unique or exceptional fitness for automobile manufacture save one: here was the home of Henry Ford and other pioneers of the industry. That fact, not geography, transformed Detroit in a single lifetime into a city renowned the world over wherever trucks and automobiles run. Had Cincinnati investors received Henry Ford's early overtures kindly, had Cleveland attracted Ransom Olds, Detroit today might be basically different."[68]

To a certain extent, New York's ascent to the top of the urban hierarchy may also be attributed to serendipitous forces. Had the British decided to sell their goods at some other port in 1815, New York's emergence as the premier commercial city would certainly have been postponed if not altogether stifled.[69] Also, Los Angeles's domination of San Diego in the 1880s was not the result of foresight and planning, nor can it be attributed to a favorable location. In fact, just the opposite is true. Los Angeles prospered because it had the good luck to be blessed with inadequate port facilities.

Although Detroit, New York, and Los Angeles were aided by luck and the adoptive behavior of the economy, the initial advantage of other cities must be attributed to those resident entrepreneurs who successfully adapted their behavior to the prevailing situation. Both Denver and Seattle, for example, were originally bypassed by the railroads. Through hard work and perseverance the local businessmen in each city overcame their initial disadvantage. As a result, Denver and not Cheyenne emerged as the dominant metropolitan center along the eastern slope of the Rocky Mountains, and Seattle, not Tacoma, became the capital of the Pacific Northwest.[70]

Civic boosterism coupled with chicanery accounts for San Francisco's emergence as the first Pacific transhipment center.

> Before early 1847 the city was known as Yerba Buena rather than San Francisco. In order to identify its own fortunes with the more famous mission and bay of San Francisco, which appeared on maritime maps throughout the world, the cove settlement changed its name to San Francisco. . . . When the Gold Rush began, San Francisco benefitted considerably. Since San Francisco Bay and mission were widely known, Eastern shippers merely sent their merchandise to San Francisco. The change of name ensured that goods would be consigned specifically to the formerly unknown hamlet of Yerba Buena rather than to the bay area in general.[71]

New York businessmen engaged in adaptive behavior when they initiated the first regularly scheduled packet service between the United States and Liverpool.[72] They also encouraged construction of the Erie Canal to ensure that New York would have the best commercial access to the interior. Similarly, Baltimore,[73] Chicago,[74] and Kansas City[75] developed extensive rail networks so they could control the trade flows within their hinterland and reduce their rival's sphere of influence.

Despite the advantage of being first, the benefits of an initial advantage have often been transitory. As economies of scale become widespread and production becomes routinized, the city with the initial advantage may no longer offer the most viable location.

As a result, the industry may disappear from the site of its inception and maturation. For example, in a study of the electronics industry in the New York metropolitan region, Hund reports that many firms moved to other locations after mass production reduced the need for skilled labor and one-of-a-kind components.[76] Under these circumstances, an initial advantage provides no guarantee that a city will continue to prosper. Instead, once the production process matures, it may relocate to a city whose factor costs are more conducive to mass production technologies. Unless the city can replace these lost activities, large-scale economies and initial advantage may signal the beginning of urban decline.

Localization Economies

In many instances, the presence of one firm attracts other firms in that industry to the same site. They agglomerate because they believe that their joint location will reduce everyone's cost of production. If these cost reductions exceed the disadvantages associated with concentration (higher wages, increased threats of unionization, higher transportation costs, etc.) then localization economies will induce concentration. Several factors account for the lower processing costs associated with localization economies.

The Habit of Industrial Imitation. If an entrepreneur succeeds in a community, then "his success proves that the economic conditions are favorable—that he is within the possible area of that industry."[77] In other words, the probability that a new firm will be "adopted" is enhanced by the knowledge that other firms have also been adopted or that they successfully adapted themselves to the local environment. Therefore, the success of one firm encourages other, less venturesome entrepreneurs to imitate both the location and production methods of the original producer. Consequently, by force of imitation, a city with an initial advantage will often attract other firms in that industry. Through this process, cities become production centers for a particular commodity or industry and their prosperity becomes linked to that industry's growth.

Labor Market Advantages. Economists have identified three labor market advantages that create localization economies. First, firms that require large numbers of skilled workers often discover that a sufficient pool is available only in large metropolitan centers. This restricts the firms' choice of feasible locations, but since every firm in the industry faces the same constraint, they are all restricted to the same limited alternatives. The result is industrial concentration. Second, by locating in a city where the labor force has already been trained by other firms, the new firm can obtain a skilled labor supply at minimal expense. "In contrast, the development of like facilities in a new area usually means starting from scratch on a lengthy and costly build-up of the labor force."[78] Finally, concentrating several firms in one location reduces the problem of labor market instability and allows each firm to adjust its labor force to accommodate sudden shifts in demand.[79] For example, when many firms in the same industry locate in one city, workers have a greater incentive to change jobs. At the same time, industrial concentration ensures a ready supply of replacements. With industrial dispersion, there may be fewer sources of alternate employment and less turnover, but finding replacements for those workers who do quit will involve relatively large recruitment and training outlays.

The Structure of Transport Rates. When transport costs were high, very few commodities could absorb the cost associated with long distance hauls. This produced a location pattern that reflected the dispersion of population and raw materials. Also, high transport rates acted as protective tariffs, shielding the inefficient producers from the competition of rivals in distant cities. Even the cost reductions associated with localization economies could not penetrate the barrier erected by high transport rates. However, as transport rates fell and long hauls became relatively less expensive, firms in a few centrally located cities could supply distant markets. This allowed them to exploit the cost reductions associated with localization economies. In other words, as transport rates dropped, agglomeration became feasible as well as desirable.

Panel A in Figure 2.8 illustrates a situation in which localization economies will not induce agglomeration.[80] P_1, P_2, and P_3 represent three production sites. A circle has been drawn around each site indicating the maximum distance the particular item can be transported. Beyond this circle, the firm will refuse to sell because of the onerous burden of freight absorption or buyers will refuse to purchase because of the exorbitant delivered price. Since the circles do not intersect, there is no common location where all three firms can operate without losing customers. Therefore, agglomeration is impossible, and each firm forfeits the benefits of localization economies.

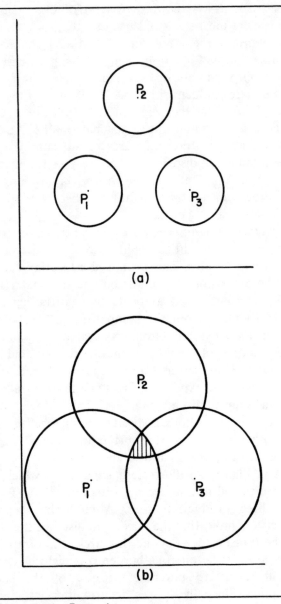

Figure 2.8: Localization Economies

In panel B, lower transport costs increase the distance that the commodity can be shipped and allow the circles to intersect. By moving to the intersection, the lower processing costs produced by localization economies will more than offset the additional transport costs. Under these conditions, agglomeration will occur.

Unfortunately, panel B only illustrates the conditions that permit agglomeration. It does not offer a realistic analysis of where agglomeration will take place or the process of agglomeration. In the first place, the diagram assumes that locations require no fixed investment or infrastructure. The firm can locate anywhere it chooses since the costs of site preparation are zero. However, in the real world, no firm will abandon its present location at an already developed site in order to develop a new low-cost site. Therefore, Isard argues correctly that firms will only seek existing production points as centers of agglomeration.

> As new units of production come into existence, they will tend to gain localization economies by agglomerating around established production points. Thereby, they frequently strengthen the gravitational pull of these points. From this standpoint, the evolutionary framework becomes critical as a locational factor; and any pure substitution theory which is not linked to specific regional structure is of severely limited significance. . . . To put it another way, the accumulated fixed investments of an urban mass in conjunction with its vested social institutions entail major geographic immobilities and rigidities and, for the most part, tend to preclude urban relocation.[81]

In addition to underestimating the rigidities blocking relocation and agglomeration, panel B assumes that firms will agglomerate when the localization economies exceed the transport diseconomies. However, even if we ignore the first set of objections, this scenario offers only a partial enumeration of the costs associated with the decision to relocate. A firm that abandons one site also forfeits its fixed investment in plant and equipment. This loss must be entered on the debit side of the ledger. In addition, the firm will incur additional costs at the new site in the form of site preparation and new plant construction. This too must be entered as a debit. Therefore, unless the old equipment has been completely depreciated and site preparation costs are zero, the tradeoff between processing costs and transport costs will not prompt relocation and agglomeration. Instead, a firm will relocate only if the savings at the new location offset both the capital costs and transport costs.[82]

Urbanization Economies

Localization economies attract several firms in one industry to a common production site. Urbanization economies attract firms in several different industries to a common production site. According to classical location theory, the concentration of firms in several industries reduces both transport costs and production costs and offers a powerful incentive for agglomeration.

Transport cost savings result from the close proximity between interdependent firms. If intermediate goods producers locate in one region while their customers establish factories in another region, then the intermediate goods will have to be shipped from the point of production to the point of consumption. By locating in the same city, these freight charges can be reduced.

Urbanization economies lower processing costs by facilitating a more extensive division of labor that allows all components of the production process to operate at the most efficient scale.[83] In a small town, for example, every aspect of the production process must be internalized within the firm. If this cannot be accomplished, the firm must eliminate that function or import it from some other city and incur the transport cost burden. But if the same firm locates in a large metropolitan area, those functions which cannot be internalized can be subcontracted to specialists who operate at the most efficient scale of production. In this fashion, the firm obtains all inputs at the lowest possible cost and gains a competitive edge over its rivals. Thus, cities whose industrial mix promotes urbanization economies will attract new firms and grow rapidly. Cities that are in no position to offer urbanization economies will stagnate.

Despite the cost reductions they create, urbanization economies, like localization economies, will not induce mass relocation. The capital costs associated with the decision to move preclude this behavior. Yet this does not mean that urbanization economies have no impact on the site selection process. In several cases, they are extremely important. For example, an entrepreneur must often weigh the advantages of a metropolitan location against the advantage of a more isolated site. In this situation, urbanization economies may influence the final decision. Those activities that rely upon urbanization economies will remain in large urban areas despite the high rents and wages associated with these locations. Those activities that are more standardized and can produce internally all the supporting functions at the most economical scale will exhibit little affinity for a metropolitan location.

Besides influencing the location decision, urbanization economies may explain why certain firms succeed and others fail. Those firms located in an area endowed with urbanization economies will operate more efficiently and at a lower total cost. Those not so fortunate will be destroyed by competition.

Although urbanization economies are usually associated with large cities, not all metropolitan areas provide a favorable environment for firms whose survival depends upon the existence of urbanization economies. In a region dominated by several large, mass production industries, it may appear that the industrial structure will provide a hospitable environment for the establishment of a new, nonstandardized line of work. Such an area often contains such supporting services as law firms, financial advisors, sources of capital, a well-trained labor force, parts suppliers, etc. Yet if these peripheral activities service only the dominant industry, they will not be geared to providing services on the small scale required by the new industry. Consequently, although the necessary services are present, they will not be available to all segments of the local economy.[84]

INDUSTRIAL DISPERSION

Agglomeration economies centralize industry in a few locations. They induce firms to ignore the site that minimizes transport outlays and promise reductions in processing costs that more than offset the additional transport costs. However, other factors also affect processing costs but their influence promotes industrial dispersion, not agglomeration. Among the factors that counteract the agglomeration tendencies are such items as labor costs, the local tax burden, and government subsidies.

Labor Cost Differentials

The development of cheap transportation facilities released many manufacturing processes from their former ties to large cities. Businessmen have discovered that by shifting certain segments of the manufacturing process to low-wage areas while maintaining other functions in the central city, they can have the best of both worlds. Those activities that require urbanization and localization economies will retain their ties to the city despite its high land and labor costs while other activities with fewer claims to an inner-city location will move to the area promising the greatest savings in labor costs. With this arrangement, businessmen obtain the greatest reduction in total costs while preserving the advantage of a metropolitan location. Thus, labor cost differentials can displace a firm from the site that minimizes transport outlays and also from the site which, as a result of urbanization and localization economies, promises some reduction in processing costs. In terms of Isard's substitution analysis, we can state that a firm will locate in an area where labor costs are lowest if the savings in labor costs are sufficient to offset the added transportation expenses and the loss of certain agglomeration economies.

Labor cost variations result from two factors. First, some areas have a lower cost of living. In these areas, workers can achieve the same standard of living even though they are paid less than workers residing in high cost of living regions. Second, regional variations in labor militancy, productivity, and labor laws create real wage differentials. However, irrespective of their cause, wage disparities influence the location of industry and the rate of urban growth.

Cost of Living. Even if real wages are equal, firms searching for a cheap labor site will locate in the region with the lowest cost of living. This tendency will be especially pronounced if the manufacturing process requires large quantities of unskilled labor and if the firm sells its product on a national market. When these conditions prevail, businessmen can maximize profits by reducing their dollar outlay for the various factors of production. That site with the lowest cost of living will, under the assumption of equal real wages, also be the site where dollar outlays can be minimized. Thus, it will attract a large share of labor-oriented industries.

Table 2.4 presents cost of living data for a selected group of Northeast and Sunbelt cities. For each city, Table 2.4 lists three hypothetical budgets representing different standards of living for a family of four. For all three budgets, a Sunbelt family can receive the same standard of living for less money than is possible in the Northeast. Consequently, the Sunbelt should be an attractive location for firms interested in minimizing labor costs.

Real Wages. Real wage differentials can arise from interregional variations in labor productivity, unionization, labor laws, and surplus labor. However, evidence accumulated over the past thirty years indicates conclusively that productivity differentials must be discounted as a factor contributing to interregional variations in real wages. In fact, recent evidence suggests that today southern labor productivity may actually exceed that of northern workers. A 1951 landmark study conducted by Hoover and Ratchford reported that "low labor productivity is not an innate characteristic of southern labor. Man for man, using the same ratio of economic resources and with equally good management, southern labor can produce approximately as efficiently as non-southern labor."[85] Two years earlier, in a report commissioned by the National Planning

TABLE 2.4   Family Budgets by Standard of Living by SMSA, 1970

City	Lower Level	Intermediate Level	Higher Level
NORTHEAST			
Boston	7,351	12,037	17,819
Buffalo	7,022	11,425	16,424
New York-Northeastern New Jersey	7,183	12,134	18,545
Philadelphia	6,958	10,875	15,845
Pittsburgh	6,701	10,236	14,876
Baltimore	7,018	10,580	13,590
Washington, D.C.	7,242	11,047	16,125
Chicago-Northeastern Ind.	7,273	11,120	16,019
Cincinnati	6,611	10,220	14,329
Cleveland	7,080	11,184	15,897
Detroit	6,931	10,588	15,460
Indianapolis	7,101	10,892	15,620
Kansas City	6,981	10,599	15,575
Milwaukee	7,079	11,405	16,575
Minneapolis-St. Paul	7,140	10,897	15,808
St. Louis	6,937	10,546	15,125
SUNBELT			
Atlanta	6,426	9,523	13,765
Austin	6,197	9,212	13,337
Dallas	6,683	9,894	14,471
Houston	6,481	9,645	13,917
Orlando	6,562	9,469	13,679
San Diego	7,166	10,467	15,309
U.S. metropolitan average	7,061	10,933	15,971
Average for Northeast SMSAs	7,102	10,996	15,897
Average for Sunbelt SMSAs	6,585	9,701	14,079

SOURCE: U.S. Department of Labor, Bureau of Labor Statistics, *Handbook of Labor Statistics 1971*, Bulletin 1705 (Washington DC: U.S. Government Printing Office): Table 126, Table 127, and Table 128.

Association, McLaughlin and Robock reached similar conclusions. They quote one rubber company executive who declared, "Productivity is just as good if not better in our Southern plant." Also, an official of a major electric appliance manufacturing company told them, "Although we originally had some doubts about labor productivity in the South, our experience has revealed a high efficiency of Southern labor."[86]

In the intervening years since those earlier studies were published, new manufacturing facilities have blossomed in the South while investment has lagged in the North. As a result, southern workers employ the most modern, up-to-date equipment and production techniques while northern workers are hampered by outmoded, less productive facilities. This, in turn, would suggest that today southern employees are probably more productive than Northern workers.

The higher productivity of southern labor becomes especially noticeable during recessions when firms schedule production cutbacks. Then, manufacturers shut down their least productive facilities first and concentrate the remaining output in their higher-productivity, low-unit-cost plants. During the last recession, this practice resulted in earlier and longer closings in the North and shorter layoffs in the South. According to the *Wall Street Journal,* which discussed this phenomenon in an article entitled "Sick Cities: Many Municipalities Lag Behind the Rest of the Nation in Recovering from Economic Downturn," the principal reason for shorter layoffs in the South is that region's higher labor productivity.[87] Economist Lew Mandell also referred to the higher productivity of southern labor when he told an interviewer for *Iron Age,* "All other things being equal, you can get people [of equal productivity] to work for less money [in the South], or for the same amount of money, you can get better qualified employees."[88]

If there are disparities in the degree of labor organization, then regional inequalities in real wages may coexist with equal productivity. *Business Week,* for instance, reported that "North Carolina, where industrial jobs that offer low wages are mushrooming, ranked last among the 50 states in 1974 with 6.9% of its work force unionized. In contrast, industry has been moving out of states with high rates of unionization: Michigan (38.4%), New York (38%), and Pennsylvania (37.5%)."[89] Moreover, it reported that "not only have smaller companies by the hundreds escaped unions by moving South, but major companies in the rubber, autos, and electrical equipment industries, among others, also have been spotting plants outside the Northern strongholds."

In addition to low levels of unionization, many of the Sunbelt states have enacted labor legislation designed to insure a "good business climate." Except for Louisiana, Kentucky, and New Mexico, every state in the Sunbelt has some form of "right to work" legislation. Besides making it more difficult for unions to organize, these states require less stringent labor safeguards. According to McLaughlin and Robock," one textile company states that its decision to locate a new plant in the south was in part influenced by the fact that the employment of women for longer hours was permitted in the new southern plant."[90] This legislation has not only reduced the incidence of unions, but it has also reduced the labor time lost to strikes (Table 2.5). Although both regions experienced similar cyclical variations in strike activity, strikes were less prevalent in Sunbelt states than in Northeastern states.

The large pool of available workers represents an additional factor that could depress real wages in the Sunbelt. One recent study of the economic development potential in the South reported:

> [T]he prospective decline of employment in agriculture and probably also in textile, sawmilling, and personal services and the natural rates of growth in the population of working age indicate that the South will have an ample supply of labor in the years ahead available for employment in manufacturing and service producing industries. . . . In the past the South's ample supply of non-union labor that could be hired at low wages has been a strong attraction for those industries that used large amounts of unskilled labor or labor that could be quickly trained to perform routine jobs.[91]

Displaced agricultural workers moving to urban centers are a particularly important factor contributing to lower real wages. Lewis has shown that with large supplies of surplus agricultural labor, workers in manufacturing do not have to be paid the value of their marginal product, only the value of their average

TABLE 2.5   Percentage of Estimated Total Working Time Lost Due
to Strikes

	Percentage of Estimated Total Working Time				Percentage of Estimated Total Working Time		
	1956	1963	1969		1956	1963	1969
Alabama	1.00	.12	.18	Connecticut	.26	.13	.28
Arizona	.25	.09	.04	Illinois	.22	.11	.24
Arkansas	.16	.04	.10	Indiana	.65	.16	.36
Florida	.09	.24	.26	Massachusetts	.20	.12	.39
Georgia	.09	.12	.19	Michigan	.22	.12	.22
Mississippi	.04	.01	.10	New Jersey	.29	.13	.19
New Mexico	.05	.21	.06	New York	.22	.19	.29
North Carolina	.12	.01	.06	Ohio	.66	.12	.37
Oklahoma	.13	.02	.15	Pennsylvania	.87	.16	.35
South Carolina	.13	.04	.04	Rhode Island	.05	.10	.48
Texas	.17	.10	.35	Average			
Average Sunbelt	.20	.09	.14	Northeast	.36	.13	.31
U.S. average	0.29	.13	.28				

SOURCE: U.S. Department of Labor, Bureau of Labor Statistics, *Handbook of Labor Statistics 1971*, Bulletin 1705 (Washington DC: U.S. Government Printing Office): Table 149.

productivity in agriculture.[92] If this principle operates in the Sunbelt, then the pool of native rural workers as well as Mexican immigrants, will prevent wages from rising to a level consistent with productivity. Thus, as a result of all these factors, it is conceivable that real wages in the Sunbelt are less than those in the Northeast. As long as this condition prevails, businessmen in search of a cheap labor location will choose the Sunbelt, not the Northeast.

Although we have only presented some intuitive support for the hypothesis that real wages in the Sunbelt are below those of the Northeast, the existence of money wage differentials is beyond question, and this fact by itself can account for the location of low wage industries in the South. If these money wage disparities'also reflect regional differences in real wages, then the attraction of the Sunbelt will be strengthened.

Table 2.6 presents the average hourly wage for manufacturing production workers for a selected group of northeastern and

TABLE 2.6   Average Hourly Wage Rates for Production Workers on
Manufacturing Payrolls by Selected Metropolitan Areas,
1969, 1972, 1974

| | Northeast | | | | Sunbelt | | |
	1969	1972	1974		1969	1972	1974
Chicago	3.50	4.27	missing	Austin	2.50	3.04	3.39
New York	3.22	3.92	4.46	Atlanta	3.22	3.91	4.20
Baltimore	3.33	4.08	4.78	Charlotte	2.43	2.76	3.18
Boston	3.27	3.99	4.55	Dallas	2.90	3.28	3.80
Detroit	4.17	5.29	6.00	Ft. Lauderdale-			
Cleveland	3.73	4.52	5.23	Hollywood	2.78	3.34	3.76
Pittsburgh	3.63	4.48	5.38	Fort Worth	3.21	3.63	4.13
Buffalo	3.72	4.64	5.42	Miami	2.60	3.10	3.53
Cincinnati	3.33	4.14	4.81	Phoenix	3.13	3.89	4.44
Jersey City	3.31	3.95	4.54	San Antonio	2.43	2.76	3.18
Louisville	3.45	4.33	5.04	San Diego	3.91	4.42	4.72
Milwaukee	3.69	4.50	5.25	Tampa-St.			
Minneapolis-				Petersburg	2.77	3.40	4.01
St. Paul	3.43	4.31	4.95	Orlando	2.75	3.14	3.88
Newark	3.28	3.98	4.64	Tucson	3.14	3.80	4.54
Philadelphia	3.37	4.05	4.58				
Rochester	3.61	4.49	5.12	Average for			
St. Louis	3.59	4.34	5.00	Sunbelt	2.97	3.49	3.97
Washington, DC	3.54	4.51	5.20				
Providence	2.71	3.17	3.62				
Kansas City	3.20	4.18	4.87				
Average for							
Northeast	3.47	4.26	4.92				
U.S. average	3.19	3.81	4.41				

SOURCE: For 1969 data – U.S. Department of Labor, Bureau of Labor Statistics,
Employment and Earnings: States and Areas, 1939-1969, Bulletin 1370-7: Table 16;
for 1972 data – U.S. Department of Labor, Bureau of Labor Statistics, *Employment
and Earnings: States and Areas, 1939-1972*, Bulletin 1370-10: Table 4; for 1974 data
– U.S. Department of Labor, Bureau of Labor Statistics, *Employment and Earnings:
States and Areas, 1939-1974*, Bulletin 1370-11: Table 4.

Sunbelt metropolitan areas. The data reveal a growing gap both
in absolute and relative terms. For instance in 1969, the absolute wage differential was 50¢ or 15.6% of the U.S. average
manufacturing wage. By 1972 the gap had increased to 77¢ or

20.3% of the national average and by 1974 it widened to 95¢ or 21.5% of the U.S. average manufacturing wage.

While there is no doubt that businessmen are attracted to the South because of its docile, low-wage, unorganized labor force, the concentration of low-wage industries in this region has not been the major factor supporting the South's rapid growth. The dynamics of urban development in the South and the impact of wage disparities can be better understood if we first divide the manufacturing sector into two components. Those sectors in which employment declined or increased at a slower rate than the U.S. average for all manufacturing comprise the below-average growth component. As of 1960, these industries, with but one exception, offered an average hourly wage that was less than the U.S. average hourly manufacturing wage. The remaining manufacturing industries are assigned to the above average growth component and, as of 1960, they also comprised the above-average wage segment. Thus, slow-growing industries are generally associated with low wages and rapidly growing industries with high wages.

Once this division is made, several interesting points emerge. First, many of those sectors included in the below average growth category declined nationally although they grew by an average of 15% in the South. Thus, as a result of its lower pay scale, the South has captured a significant share of the low-wage manufacturing industries and, in some activities it now accounts for as much as 60% to 70% of the national employment. Since these same industries have been declining nationally while expending regionally, the South has gained the reputation as a haven for the low-wage components of manufacturing. But as of 1960, low-wage industries accounted for only 40% of the South's manufacturing employment.

However, among fast-growing, high-wage industries, the South's performance was even more outstanding. Industries with an above-average growth rate expanded by 92% nationally but by 180% in the South. Moreover, between 1940 and 1960, southern manufacturing employment grew by approximately

1,560,000 jobs. Almost 90% of these gains occurred in the above-average growth, high-wage group of industries.

Thus, it would be misleading to attribute southern growth simply to the relocation of low-paying industries from the Northeast to the Sunbelt. This factor may account for a significant share of the recent decline in the older metropolitan areas, but it does not account for the great bulk of southern manufacturing growth. Clearly this region is more than a low-wage carbon copy of the industrial Northeast, and its growth has not been limited solely to those low-wage sectors that are looking for a cheaper labor site. Rather, because of its lower pay scales and less stringent labor laws, the South had emerged as a lower-wage site for traditionally high-wage activities.

Taxes and Location

Business Taxes. In the past few years, businessmen have argued that high business taxes have induced industry to locate in lower tax jurisdictions. They claim that the economic decline and loss of jobs will halt only when these cities cut their taxes and improve their business climate. For example, a recent article in the *Wall Street Journal* warned that "Many cities that are economically in trouble—recovering slowly from the recent recession or trapped in a long term decline, or both—levy taxes so high that the competitiveness of local companies often is impaired. In Los Angeles, for example, businessmen complain that they are hurt by the city's gross receipts and inventory levies, which other nearby cities don't have. Towns in Connecticut have lured companies away from New York City with the siren call of sharply lower taxes."[93] In other words, the business community believes that tax increases are self-defeating. They strangle the most productive elements within the local economy and induce businessmen to locate elsewhere. This requires higher tax rates to generate the same revenue, but the higher rates only accelerate the business exodus and erosion of the tax base.

Although businessmen claim that tax rates significantly influence their location decisions, various studies contradict their claim. Alyea, for instance, concluded that tax rates are a minor factor in location decisions and that taxes do not drive capital from an area. In a survey of relocating plants, he found that businessmen ranked tax considerations eleventh on a list of sixteen possible location criteria.[94] McLaughlin and Robock agree with Alyea. Their study found that "tax differentials are important in selecting one location over another only in the last stage of the analysis when it is a question of picking one of two or three possible localities."[95]

To resolve this apparent contradiction between businessmen's public assertions and their actual behavior, we must distinguish between the decision to relocate and the decision either to expand or construct a new factory. Clearly, a firm will not relocate simply to reduce its tax burden. If it did relocate in response to tax stimuli, the firm would incur the added cost of reconstructing its assets in a new location. Unless the tax savings offset these costs, tax considerations by themselves will not prompt relocation. However, once the firm has decided, on other grounds, that a move is warranted, and after it has narrowed its choice to one or two equally desirable sites, then the question of relative tax burdens may influence the final decision.

If viewed from this perspective, we see that differential tax rates can have a serious impact on the economic viability of the northeastern metropolitan areas. A recent study commissioned by the New York State Department of Commerce showed that one-third of the manufacturing plants in the state are obsolete, with a useful life of less than five years. It is this obsolescence and not the high tax rates which place New York at a competitive disadvantage. But once the decision to construct new facilities has been made, New York's high tax burden enters into the decision calculus. Businessmen can either rebuild in New York State or they can decide to move their operations to a new region. Since the construction costs must be incurred wherever they locate, the relative tax burdens will be sufficient, in some cases, to tip the decision against continuing at the old site. In this manner, the highly taxed Northeast is placed at a competitive disadvantage with respect to the Sunbelt. Moreover, high tax burdens not only prompt the exodus of business, but they also deter new firms from locating in this region. Thus, because of high taxes some firms with obsolete plants leave while others fail to consider the Northeast as a potential location. This last point was recently underscored by John Dyson, the New York State Commerce Commissioner, who declared, "What they don't know and don't see are the plants we don't get, the ones that are built in the South and the West because businessmen don't want to stay in New York. As a result, our plants and equipment are getting more and more obsolete. They become less competitive and eventually they have to be closed, leaving people without jobs."[96]

Personal Taxes. Besides high payroll taxes, corporate income taxes, and property taxes on commercial facilities, these same regions also place high taxes on personal income and property. As a result, many firms in these regions find it difficult to recruit managerial and technical personnel. For instance, *Business Week* recently reported that "Data General Corp., a fast growing minicomputer producer in Southboro, Massachusetts, will soon announce that it is relocating its research, development, and engineering center to a new facility in North Carolina. The company cited its inability to attract the large number of professionals it needs because of the high cost of living and high taxes in Massachusetts. . . . The prospect of a graduated income tax, to be voted on in November, which would increase taxes for those earning over $20,000 is viewed as a significant threat."[97]

The effect of personal income taxes on the local cost of living is underscored by Bureau of Labor Statistics data which calculate the relative weight of personal income taxes in the higher level budget for a family of four. In Boston, for example, the higher level budget is 15% above the average budget for all metropolitan areas but personal income taxes are 28% above the national metropolitan average. Similarly, New York City's budget is 20% above average while taxes are 42% higher than average. By contrast, the budget in Dallas is 7% below average and taxes are 21% below the national metropolitan norm. In Atlanta, the comparable figures are 11% and 18% below the national average.[98] Thus, rather than pay the higher salaries necessary to offset the added tax burden and higher cost of living, businessmen have decided to relocate the high-wage sector of their operations to the relatively lower-taxed metropolitan centers in the Sunbelt.

Local Business Subsidies

The recent decision of the Volkswagen Corporation to establish an auto assembly plant in New Stanton, Pennsylvania, has raised many questions concerning the use of subsidies to lure business to a region. According to then Governor Milton Shapp, the decision to locate in Pennsylvania rather than Ohio was made after Pennsylvania authorities agreed to pay the entire $40 million cost for the purchase of the plant. All told, Pennsylvania had to develop a $200 million financing plan before Volkswagen would agree to the Pennsylvania site.[99]

Historically, government subsidies have taken four forms:[100]

(1) Tax credits and forgiveness. With this device the local jurisdiction either reduces or eliminates property and income taxes for a specified period after the firm has moved to its new location.

(2) Loan Guarantees. States employing this device usually establish industrial finance authorities which guarantee on behalf of the state repayment of all or part of the loan needed to finance the new facilities. Since the repayment guarantee reduces the lender's risk, the corporation is charged a lower interest rate. The subsidy to the corporation is the difference between the interest the firm would have paid without the guarantee and the lower interest it pays with the guarantee.

(3) Low Interest Loans. With this subsidy mechanism, the state uses its credit rating to borrow money and then lends these funds to firms

who locate within its borders. Generally, firms requesting this type of subsidy have been denied long- and short-term financing by the conventional capital markets.

(4) Industrial Development Bonds. In this situation, the bonds are used to finance construction of industrial development projects, sports facilities, docks, wharves, airports, sewage and waste disposal facilities, and air and water pollution equipment. Because they have been issued by the state or local government, they are granted tax free status and carry a lower interest rate.

Despite the popularity of these devices, their use has been condemned by many location theorists. In essence, they force communities to compete by offering subsidies to industry. As long as one region or locality employs these devices, all municipalities, if they are to remain competitive, must also offer subsidies. Business firms, in other words, are now paid to locate at a particular site.

Although these payments are essential within the present context of interurban and interregional competition, they are totally unproductive from a national point of view. Firms will locate somewhere with or without incentives. No new firms will exist because of these subsidies. "All you're doing is distorting locational decisions. You're not creating any new industry, just moving it someplace different."[101] Moreover, these devices represent the highest form of parasitic behavior. As one New Jersey official remarked, "What the South has been doing to New Jersey for 15 years, I'm now doing to New York. It's cutthroat regrettably, but it's every state for itself."[102]

NOTES

1. Walter Isard, *Location and Space Economy* (Cambridge, MA: MIT Press, 1956): 53. See also John Friedman, "Economy and Space: A review Article," *Economic Development and Cultural Change* 6, 3 (1958): 249-255.

2. Isard, op. cit.: 85.

3. Ibid.: 94.

4. The most comprehensive discussion of these two branches of location theory can be found in Melvin Greenhut, *Plant Location in Theory and Practice* (Chapel Hill: Univ. of North Carolina Press, 1954). For a less detailed analysis, see D. M. Smith, "A Theoretical Framework for Geographical Studies of Industrial Location," *Economic Geography* 42, 2 (1966): 95-114.

5. For a translation of Von Thunen's treatise, see Peter Hall (ed.), *Von Thunen's Isolated State* (Oxford: Pergamon, 1966).

6. C. J. Friedrich (trans.), *Alfred Weber's Theory of the Location of Industries* (Chicago: Univ. of Chicago Press, 1928).

7. Edgar Hoover, *Location Theory and the Shoe and Leather Industry* (Cambridge, MA: Harvard Univ. Press, 1937).

8. Greenhut, op. cit.: 258.

9. This assumption is necessary only to simplify the geometrical representation of least cost location theory. It is not a necessary requirement of the theory.

10. Harold Hotelling, "Stability in Competition," *Economic Journal* 39 (March 1929): 41-57.

11. Frank A. Fetter, "The Economic Law of Market Areas," *Quarterly Journal of Economics* 38, 4 (1928): 520-529.

12. Abba Lerner and Harry Singer, "Some Notes on Duopoly and Spatial Competition," *Journal of Political Economy* 45, 2 (1937): 145-186.

13. Arthur F. Smithies, "Optimum Location In Spatial Competition," *Journal of Political Economy* 49, 3 (1941): 423-439.

14. Edward Chamberlain, *The Theory of Monopolistic Competition*, 5th edition (Cambridge, MA: Harvard Univ. Press, 1946): Appendix G.

15. Greenhut, op. cit.: 258.

16. Peter Hall, op. cit.: 8.

17. Ibid.: 8.

18. August Losch, *The Economics of Location* (New Haven, CT: Yale Univ. Press, 1954): 38.

19. Edgar Dunn, *The Location of Agricultural Production* (Gainesville: Univ. of Florida Press, 1954): 38.

20. For a definition of this term and an example of its relationship to Von Thunen's theory, see J. T. Schlebecker, "The World Metropolis and the History of American Agriculture," *Journal of Economic History* 20, 2 (1960): 187-208. Also see J. Richard Peet, "The Spatial Expansion of Commercial Agriculture In The Nineteenth Century: A Von Thunen Interpretation," *Economic Geography* 45, 4 (1969): 283-301.

21. Schlebecker, op. cit.: 193.

22. Losch, op. cit.: 51.

23. Julius Rubin, "Urban Growth and Regional Development," in David T. Gilchrist (ed.), *The Growth of the Seaport Cities* (Charlottesville: Univ. of Virginia Press, 1967): 10.

24. Allen R. Pred, *Urban Growth and the Circulation of Information* (Cambridge, MA: Harvard Univ. Press, 1973): 114.

25. George R. Taylor, *The Transportation Revolution* (New York: Holt, Rinehart & Winston, 1964): 133.

26. Ibid.: 160.

27. Schlebecker, op. cit.: 201.

28. See Fred A. Shannon, *The Farmers' Last Frontier: Agriculture, 1860-1897* (New York: Farrar & Rinehart, 1945): 163. In addition to Shannon, other sources that describe the shift in agricultural zones are Chapters 6-12 in Paul W. Gates, *The Farmer's Age: Agriculture, 1815-1860* (New York: Holt, Rinehart & Winston, 1960); and Earl D. Ross, "The Emergence of Agricultural Regionalism," in Harold F. Williamson (ed.), *The Growth of the American Economy* (New York: Prentice-Hall, 1944): 379-410.

29. Schlebecker, op. cit.: 203.

30. Quoted in Thomas Cochran and William Miller, *The Age of Enterprise* (New York: Harper & Row, 1961): 57.

31. For a more complete explanation of Von Thunen's theory of rent, see Arthur H. Leigh, "Von Thunen's Theory of Distribution and the Advent of Marginal Analysis," *Journal of Political Economy* 54, 6 (1946): 481-502.

32. Peter Hall, op. cit.: xxv.

33. Ibid.: xxx.

34. For a complete discussion of capital intensity and agricultural zones, see Richard Kryzmowski, "A Graphical Presentation of Thunen's Theory of Intensity," *Journal of Farm Economics* 10, 4 (1928): 461-482.

35. For a comprehensive review of this literature see Clarence Danhoff, "Agricultural Technology To 1880," in Harold Williamson (ed.), op. cit.: 113-140; Paul W. Gates, op. cit.: Chapter 13; Shannon, op. cit.: Chapter 6; Clarence Danhoff, "Farm Making Costs and the Safety Valve: 1850-1860," *Journal of Political Economy* 49, 3 (1941): 317-359. An analysis of the relationship between farm mechanization and distance from a metropolitan center is available in Donald J. Bogue, *The Structure of the Metropolitan Community* (New York: Russel & Russel, 1971).

36. For example, see Richard Haig, "The Assignment of Activities To Areas In Urban Regions," *Quarterly Journal of Economics* 40, 4 (1926): 402-434; Howard J. Nelson, "The Form and Structure of Cities: Urban Growth Patterns," in Robert Putnam, Frank Taylor, and Philip Kettle (eds.), *A Geography of Urban Places* (Toronto: Methuen, 1970): 101-110; and Martin Reinemann, "The Pattern and Distribution of Manufacturing In The Chicago Area," in Putnam, Taylor, Kettle (eds.), op. cit.: 111-116.

37. See William Alonso, *Location and Land Use* (Cambridge, MA: Harvard Univ. Press, 1964); Richard Muth, *Cities and Housing* (Chicago: Univ. of Chicago Press, 1969); Edwin S. Mills, "Urban Density Gradients," *Urban Studies* 7, 1 (1970): 5-20; and Harold Brodsky, "Residential Land and Improvement Values In A Central City," *Land Economics* 46 (August 1970): 229-247.

38. For an excellent summary of some early studies of industrial diffusion, see Coleman Woodbury and Frank Cliffe, 'Industrial Location and Urban Redevelopment," in Coleman Woodbury (eds.), *The Future of Cities and Urban Redevelopment* (Chicago: Univ. of Chicago Press, 1953). A summary of recent studies can be found in Bennett Harrison, *Urban Economic Development* (Washington, DC: Urban Institute, 1974): Chapter 1. Also see John F. Kain, "The Distribution and Movement of Jobs and Industry," in James Q. Wilson (ed.), *The Metropolitan Enigma* (Cambridge, MA: Harvard Univ. Press, 1968): 1-43; and Brian Berry and Yehoshua S. Cohen,

"Decentralization of Commerce and Industry: The Restructuring of Metropolitan America," in Louis H. Masotti and Jeffrey K. Hadden (eds.), *The Urbanization of the Suburbs* (Beverly Hills: Sage, 1973): 431-455.

39. On this point see Sam Bass Warner, *Streetcar Suburbs* (New York: Atheneum, 1972); Robert Fogelson, *The Fragmented Metropolis: Los Angeles, 1850-1970* (Cambridge, MA: Harvard Univ. Press, 1967); George Hilton and John Due, *The Electric Interurban Railways In America* (Palo Alto: Stanford Univ. Press, 1960); and Mildred W. Walmsley, "The Bygone Electric Interurban Railway System," *Professional Geographer* 17, 1 (1965): 1-16.

40. Walter Isard, "Some Locational Factors in the Iron and Steel Industry Since the Early Nineteenth Century," *Journal of Political Economy* 56, 3 (1948): 203-217. See also Allen Rodgers, "Industrial Inertia: A Major Factor in the Location of the Steel Industry in the United States," *Geographical Review* 42, 1 (1952): 56-66.

41. The figures for 1900 steel production are from Frederick S. Hall, "The Localization of Industries," *Twelfth Census of the United States, Manufacturing, Part I* (Washington, DC: U.S. Government Printing Office, 1902): cxcviii-cxcix.

42. Constance McLaughlin Green, *American Cities In The Growth of the Nation* (New York: Harper & Row, 1965): 152. Also see Shannon, op. cit.: 227.

43. Frederick Hall, op. cit.: ccvii.

44. Benjamin Chinitz, *Freight and the Metropolis* (Cambridge, MA: Harvard Univ. Press, 1960): 94.

45. Greenhut, op. cit.: 119.

46. Isard, *Location and Space Economy:* 204.

47. Chauncy Harris, "The Market As A Factor In The Localization of Industry In The United States," *Annals of the Association of American Geographers* 44 (December 1954): 318.

48. Chinitz, op. cit.: 116-122.

49. Greenhut, op. cit.: 109.

50. Harris, op. cit.: 323 defines market potential as "the retail sales of that county divided by the transport cost of reaching the city for which the market potential is calculated."

51. A. J. Wright, "Recent Changes in the Concentration of Manufacturing," *Annals of the Association of American Geographers* 35 (January 1945): 144-166; and John Alexander, "Industrial Expansion in the United States," *Economic Geography* 28, 2 (1952): 128-142.

52. See Alfred Watkins, "Intermetropolitan Migration and the Rise of the Sunbelt," *Social Science Quarterly* 59, 3 (1978): 553-561.

53. For a more detailed theoretical discussion of the impact of transport barriers see Alonso, op. cit.: 87; and Hoover, op. cit.: 57-58.

54. The concept of an "economic hinge" was introduced by Jean Gottmann, *Megalopolis* (Cambridge, MA: MIT Press, 1961): Chapter 3. For additional information on the early mercantile relationships between seaport cities and Europe, see Robert Albion, *The Rise of the New York Port* (New York: Scribner, 1937); and Curtis P. Nettles, "The Economic Relations of Boston, Philadelphia, and New York," *Journal of Economic and Business History* 3, 2 (1930): 185-215.

55. For a discussion of the subordinate role of manufacturing in the early history of mercantile cities, see Allen Pred, *The Spatial Dynamics of U.S. Urban*

Industrial Growth, 1800-1914 (Cambridge, MA: MIT Press, 1966): Chapter 4.

56. Richard Wade, *The Urban Frontier* (Chicago: Univ. of Chicago Press, 1959) Chapter 1 presents an excellent discussion of the locational factors that prompted the growth of six western cities.

57. Lucille Kain, *The Waterfall That Built a City* (St. Paul: Minnesota Historical Society, 1966).

58. For a discussion of the economic impact of canals on urban growth, see Carter Goodrich, "Local Planning of Internal Improvements," *Political Science Quarterly* 64, 4 (1949): 355-387; Julius Rubin, *Canal or Railroad* (Philadelphia: American Philosophical Society, 1961); George Rogers Taylor, "American Urban Growth Preceding the Railway Age," *Journal of Economic History* 27, 3 (1967): 309-339; and Louis B. Schmidt, "Internal Commerce and the Development of the National Economy Before 1860," *Journal of Political Economy* 47, 6 (1939): 798-822.

59. James Weston Livingood, *The Philadelphia-Baltimore Trade Rivalry* (Harrisburg: Pennsylvania Historical and Museum Commission, 1947).

60. Wyatt Belcher, *The Economic Rivalry Between St. Louis and Chicago* (New York: Columbia Univ. Press, 1947).

61. Leonard P. Curry, *Rail Routes South* (Lexington: Univ. of Kentucky Press, 1969).

62. For additional elaboration of this point see Chinitz, op. cit.: 37-38.

63. Fogelson, op. cit.: 55.

64. Hoover, op. cit.: 90-91.

65. The delivered price is the sum of processing costs and transportation charges.

66. Isard, *Location and Space Economy:* 174. Also see Frederick Hall, op. cit.: ccxii; and Pred, *The Spatial Dynamics of U.S. Urban Industrial Growth.* Chapter 1 for a discussion of initial advantage.

67. Armen Alchian, "Uncertainty, Evolution, and Economic Theory," *Journal of Political Economy* 58, 3 (1950): 211-221. On this same point, also see Charles Tiebout, "Location Theory, Empirical Evidence, and Economic Evolution," *Papers and Proceedings of the Regional Science Association* 3 (1957): 74-86.

68. Green, op. cit.: 193.

69. Albion, op. cit.: 11.

70. Green, op. cit.: Chapter 6-7.

71. Roger Lotchin, "San Francisco: The Patterns of Chaos and Growth," in Kenneth Jackson and Stanley Schultz (eds.), *Cities In American History* (New York: Knopf, 1972): 145-146.

72. Albion, op. cit.: 15.

73. Carter Goodrich and Harvey Segal, "Baltimore's Aid to Railroads–A Study In The Municipal Planning of Internal Improvements," *Journal of Economic History* 13, 1 (1953): 2-35.

74. Belcher, op. cit.

75. Charles Glaab, *Kansas City and the Railroads* (Madison: State Historical Society of Wisconsin, 1967).

76. James M. Hund, "Electronics," in Max Hall (ed.), *Made In New York* (Cambridge, MA: Harvard Univ. Press. 1959).

77. Frederick Hall, op. cit.: ccxii.

78. Martin Segal, *Wages In The Metropolis* (Cambridge, MA: Harvard Univ. Press, 1960): 20.

79. Hoover, op. cit.: 108, declares, "A manufacturer of shoes and slippers in a large Middle Atlantic city is quoted as saying, 'Due to the fact that our business is seasonal and that we employ the greatest number of people between July and December, it is advantageous for us to be in this city. We can get the labor as we want it here even though at a higher price, and can lay our people off during the slow periods when they can usually get temporary employment elsewhere.' "

80. The diagram is adopted from Isard, *Location and Space Economy:* 177-178.

81. Ibid.: 177.

82. This analysis has been adapted from Joseph Schumpeter, *Capitalism, Socialism, and Democracy* (New York: Harper & Row, 1962): 96-98.

83. For a more extended discussion of this process, see George Stigler, "The Division of Labor Is Limited by the Extent of the Market," *Journal of Political Economy* 59, 3 (1951): 185-193; and A.W. Evans, "The Pure Theory of City Size in an Industrial Economy," *Urban Studies* 9, 1 (1972): 49-77.

84. Benjamin Chinitz, "New York and Pittsburgh: Contrasts in Agglomeration," *American Economic Review, Papers and Proceedings* 51 (May 1961): 272-289.

85. Calvin B. Hoover and B. U. Ratchford, *Economic Resources and Policies of the South* (New York: Macmillan, 1951): 66.

86. Glenn McLaughlin and Stefan Robock, *Why Industry Moves South,* National Planning Association, Committee of the South, Report Number 3 (June 1949): 74.

87. "Sick Cities: Many Municipalities Lag Behind the Rest of the Nation in Recovering from Economic Downturn," *Wall Street Journal* (June 16, 1976): 1.

88. Quoted in Jeanne C. Biggar, "The Sunning of America: Migration to the Sunbelt," *Population Bulletin* 34, 1 (Population Reference Bureau, Inc.: Washington, DC, 1979): 25.

89. "No Welcome Mats for Unions in the Sunbelt," *Business Week* (May 17, 1976): 109-110.

90. McLaughlin and Robock, op. cit.: 70.

91. James G. Maddox et al., *The Advancing South* (New York: Twentieth Century Fund, 1967): 78-79.

92. W. A. Lewis, "Economic Development with Unlimited Supplies of Labor," in A. N. Agarwala and S. P. Singh (eds.), *The Economics of Underdevelopment* (New York: Oxford Univ. Press, 1958): 400-450.

93. "Sick Cities: Municipal Leaders Try To Cure Economic Ills but the Medicine Often Worsens the Ailments," *Wall Street Journal* (June 17, 1976): 36. Also see "Cut Business Taxes New York City Urged," *New York Times* (December 13, 1976): 1.

94. Paul Alyea, quoted in Greenhut, op. cit.: 138.

95. McLaughlin and Robock, op. cit.: 107.

96. "State's Commerce Chief Asks Fiscal Shift to Right," *New York Times* (February 2, 1976): 1.

97. "Brain Drain: A Worry for New England," *Business Week* (October 25, 1976): 32.

98. All figures are from U.S. Department of Labor, Bureau of Labor Statistics, *1971 Handbook of Labor Statistics*, Bulletin 1705, Table 131.

99. "Financing Troubles For VW's New Plant," *Business Week* (July 5, 1976): 26.

100. Bennett Harrison and Sandra Kanter, "The Great State Robbery," *Working Papers for a New Society* 4 (Spring 1976): 62.

101. "A Counterattack in the War Between the States," *Business Week* (June 21, 1976): 71.

102. Ibid.: 71.

Chapter 3

MARKET AREAS AND CENTRAL PLACE THEORY

The preceding discussion ignored the relationship between product demand and location. It assumed that consumers concentrate at one point and that the firm's location could be determined solely by supply considerations. Because the least-cost approach assumes implicitly that every consumer has a demand curve with zero elasticity, the firm can ignore the influence of delivery charges on final demand and supply the entire market at the lowest possible price from the least cost location. However, if these unrealistic assumptions are modified, then the least-cost approach does not enumerate all the variables which influence the choice of a production site. For example, when delivery costs affect the shape and position of a firm's demand curve, the entrepreneur must choose a location that not only minimizes processing costs but which also maximizes total revenue. This additional complexity increases the number of variables that must be included in the substitution analysis. With a least cost approach, an entrepreneur had to be concerned only with the substitution possibilities between various components of total cost. When demand enters the analysis, the entrepreneur must also consider the substitutions between processing costs in general and total revenue.

In this section we will consider some of the revenue implications of industrial location. The discussion will be divided into four major topics—the size and shape of a firm's market area, the question of locational interdependence, the influence of various pricing strategies on a firm's market area, and the effects of "basing points" on regional development. By approaching the subject in this fashion, it will be possible for us to shed some additional light on the factors contributing to the present spatial configuration of economic activity and the forces promoting regional economic realignments.

Moreover, with the inclusion of demand variables, we can eliminate certain logical inconsistencies inherent in the least-cost approach. One of the more glaring defects concerns the analysis of agglomeration economies. That analysis outlined several theories to explain the reduction in processing costs resulting from industrial concentration and the formation of industrial belts. Other cost-reducing factors were added to the analysis to explain when a firm would leave the site offering the greatest agglomeration economies. Yet if these considerations can entice one firm away from the point of agglomeration, the remaining firms should also be motivated to relocate. By concentrating in the new region, they can all reduce their processing costs without forfeiting the advantages of agglomeration. Thus, if it is extended to its logical conclusion, the theory of agglomeration economies should explain the relocation of industrial districts but not the relocation of individual firms. Industries should move *en masse* and not in the fragmented, uncoordinated fashion that characterizes their present behavior. However, it is clear that firms do not follow the precise, logical dictates of classical location theory. Therefore, we can either conclude that they are acting irrationally or that their site selection is influenced by additional considerations such as product demand that have been ignored by least-cost analysis.

In addition, the least-cost approach ignores the influence of transport charges on final demand. Since classical location theory assumes that delivery charges have no effect on demand, a firm that has discovered the least-cost location can saturate the entire market from this one production point. If the firm requires a market orientation, then population shifts will lead to the establishment of branch plants in the midst of these new population centers. However, according to least-cost location theory, these new facilities are not constructed in order to reduce delivery charges and increase demand. Instead, they are built because a market-oriented, cost-minimizing firm must locate in the vicinity of the market.

Although at first this may appear to be a trivial issue, it suggests that least-cost theory and market area analysis offer different explanations for a firm's market orientation. The least-cost approach assumes that all freight charges are borne by the producer and represent a deduction from profits. Consequently, in their quest to minimize costs (and thereby maximize profits) producers attempt to reduce delivery charges by locating near the consumer. Market area analysis, by comparison, assumes F.O.B. pricing. Under this system, freight charges are added to the factory or mill price. They are a burden to the consumer and reduce demand. Therefore, a revenue maximizing producer will obtain the greatest market share by locating near his customers and reducing their delivered price.

Thus, both theories predict the same location but they assume completely different pricing strategies and motives. If a firm adopts some form of non F.O.B. pricing system, then market area analysis suggests that its preferred location will change. The least-cost approach, on the other hand, does not consider the explicit relationship between pricing strategies and location. Consequently, it would not predict a shift in location. Therefore, until we develop a supplement to classical location theory, many forces promoting urban development and economic decline will remain unexplored.

MARKET AREAS AND SUPPLY AREAS

The concepts and analytic techniques developed by market area analysis can be used to define the shape and extent of a city's supply area and market area.[1] With many geographically dispersed producers and one buyer (monopsony) located in a city, supply area analysis considers the effect of transport charges on the size of a city's hinterland. With two or more cities located in one region, supply area analysis determines which producers will sell to each city.

Market area analysis reverses the role of producer and consumer. Now, the city produces various commodities and its customers are located in the hinterland. With one production center and scattered consumers, market area analysis considers the influence of transport charges on delivered price and the firm's demand. When two cities attempt to sell their products to the same customers, market area analysis determines the shape and size of the city's market area. However, since market area and supply area analysis employ identical analytic techniques and arrive at the same conclusions, it is not necessary to consider them as distinct problems. Consequently, the remainder of this discussion will focus primarily on market areas and their impact on industrial location.

In Figure 3.1, two cities (A and B) compete for customers in the same hinterland. We assume that prices are set on an F.O.B. basis and that consumers purchase from the city that offers the lowest delivered price. The circles represent the delivered price (factory cost plus transport charges) at various distance zones from each city. With identical transport and production costs at each site, each city will supply exactly one half of the region. To the right of the market boundary XY, A will be unable to sell because his delivered price will exceed B's delivered price. Conversely, B will be unable to sell to the left of line XY.

In addition to depicting the market area boundary, Figure 3.1 suggests that each city is a monopolist within its portion of the hinterland. The cities compete only for market shares but once these have been established, the customers patronize only

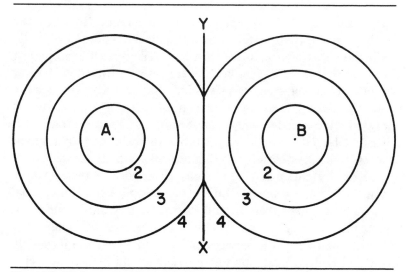

Figure 3.1: Market Areas: Identical Production and Transport Costs

one producer. However, despite this monopolistic situation, the presence of potentially competing production centers limits each city's freedom of action. For example, "if two selling markets, A and B, are geographically so situated that goods may be shipped from one to the other, obviously the prices in the two markets cannot . . . differ by more than the amount of the freight . . . between the two points. If the differences exceed that sum, the one market would destroy the other."[2] Consumers would purchase from the lowest priced producer since even after they paid the higher transport charges, the delivered price would be less than the delivered price offered by the more proximate, higher-priced producer. But as transport rates increase, each producer receives greater monopoly power and freedom to raise his factory price.

This would seem to suggest that manufacturers should have a vested interest in high freight rates and a desire to block transport improvements. By maintaining high freight charges, an artificial barrier, similar to tariffs, would shield the city's industries from the ravages of competition. It is within this context that Hotelling offers the following advice to urban businessmen:

"These particular merchants would do well, instead of organizing improvement clubs and booster associations to better the
roads, to make transportation as difficult as possible."[3]

Despite this advice, urban history is filled with examples of
local businessmen demanding better, more efficient transportation and lower freight rates. More importantly, those cities
with the lowest freight rates and most efficient transportation
networks grew faster and became more prosperous than their
rivals protected by high freight rates. How can we explain their
success in light of Hotelling's theoretically correct advice?

To resolve this paradox, we must distinguish between supply
areas and market areas. During the period when cities constructed turnpikes, canals, and railroads, mercantile functions
were the primary source of local prosperity. To expand the
quantity of mercantile services, a city had to expand its supply
area and raid its rival's hinterland. This could be accomplished
only by reducing transport barriers. However, if local manufacturers want greater monopoly power within their market area,
they can preserve their autonomy by erecting transport barriers
to block the entry of lower-priced merchandise. Thus, if the aim
is to protect the market area of high-priced, handicraft products
from price competition by mass-produced commodities, Hotelling's dictum is correct. But during the earliest phase of urban
growth, mercantile activities dominated, and during the next
stage mass production became the leading source of urban
prosperity. Consequently, Hotelling's advice, although theoretically correct, is historically uninformed.

Up to this point, we have considered the highest possible
price that a producer can charge and still retain some customers.
However, even if the firm does not raise its price to this
absolute limit, any increase relative to its competitor's price will
erode the city's market area and reduce its monopoly power.
Figure 3.2 illustrates the relative size and shape of market areas
when two cities have unequal factory prices. The market boundary is no longer a straight line. Instead, it becomes a hyperbole
"bent around the focus, or market with the higher base price
with its two sides diverging in a general direction away from the

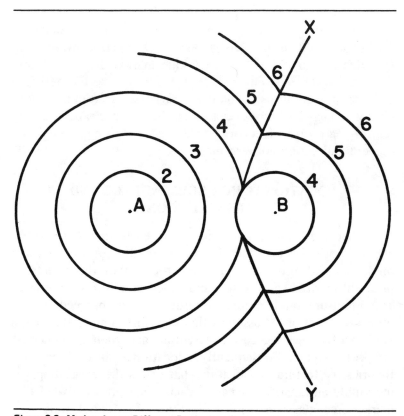

Figure 3.2: Market Areas: Different Production Costs and Identical Transport Rates

focus, or market, with the lower base price."[4] As the price differential increases, the high price city loses additional markets and the market boundary becomes a more acute hyperbole. If lower transport rates accompany these increasing price differentials, the market area of the high-price city shrinks even faster until eventually the high-price city loses all its customers.

By combining market area analysis with the earlier discussions of agglomeration economies, we can develop a more precise analysis of uneven development. Least cost analysis assumes that those firms with the lowest processing costs can eliminate their rivals. Since they can also offer a lower delivered price, they can enlarge their market area. Because of their larger market area these firms operate on a more efficient scale. This, in turn, allows them to increase the cost differential even further and obtain an even larger market area. Conversely, as the high-cost factories face shrinking market areas, they lose any large-scale economies. This increases the cost differential and prompts additional rounds of market area shrinkage. Thus, both the high-cost city and low-cost city experience mutually reinforcing positive feedback cycles that promote uneven development and inhibit convergence.

LOCATIONAL INTERDEPENDENCE AND SITE SELECTION

Market area analysis assumes that each firm has already chosen a specific location. Then, within the context of these predetermined production points, it describes the effects of price differentials on the size and shape of a firm's hinterland. The literature on locational interdependence proceeds in the opposite direction. It assumes that each firm knows the spatial pattern of processing cost differentials and their influence on market areas. Consequently, locational interdependence theories try to find the location that offers the greatest spatial monopoly and market area given each firm's prior knowledge of market area constraints and the location of potential rivals.

At first, it would appear that firms hoping to maximize their spatial monopoly should maximize the distance between themselves and their potential rivals. In this way, each receives a separate hinterland that is free from all competitive encumbrances. The transport barriers associated with industrial dispersion guarantee this autonomy and ensure that market areas overlap as little as possible.

In the case of a multiplant firm, plant dispersion is the accepted practice. Rather than concentrating all productive facilities in one location, the entrepreneur minimizes the delivered price and maximizes total revenue by distributing branch plants on the basis of population. Consumers benefit by having their orders filled from the plant with the lowest delivered price. In addition, since the market is divided into impermeable, distinct regions, this eliminates cross-hauling, a practice whereby one plant sells in the natural territory of another. Although this produces spatial monopolies, dispersion is more efficient than agglomeration since the latter requires an expensive transcontinental transportation and communications infrastructure. Thus, within the context of market area analysis, a perfectly planned economy would avoid excessive concentration and opt instead for dispersion.

An unplanned, competitive economy, however, will induce an inefficient pattern of agglomeration with excessive transport expenses and higher delivered prices. The degree of competitively induced agglomeration depends upon the elasticity of demand and the location of all potential competitors.

Hotelling, for instance, assumes an F.O.B. pricing system, an even distribution of consumers arrayed along a straight line, equal processing costs at all locations, and an infinitely inelastic demand curve.[5] He then seeks to determine the optimum locations for two competing production units. According to his analysis, if both firms choose separate quartile locations each will monopolize half of the total market, no commodity will travel more than 25% of the market length, and social welfare will be maximized. Unfortunately, this optimum distribution can never occur in a competitive market.

For example, assume that the first of two firms locates at a quartile position. The second firm can maximize its market area and total revenue by locating adjacent to the first firm and on the side nearest the middle of the market. In this position the second firm can supply 75% of the market at the lowest delivered price, while the first firm receives only the remaining 25%. Because consumers have infinitely inelastic demand curves, they will purchase the same quantity despite the higher delivered price and the firm does not have to worry about losing its most distant customers. However, this situation is less than optimal for the first firm. If relocation is costless, then the first firm will move to the other side of the second firm and increase its market share. This, in turn, will prompt a move by the

second firm and so an, ad infinitum, until both are concentrated
at the midpoint which represents the only equilibrium position.
Now, each supplies 50% of the market and neither can increase
its market share by relocating. Had they both settled at the
quartiles, however, agglomeration could have been avoided,
each firm would still have the same market share, and consumers would have benefited from a lower average delivered
price. Therefore, according to Hotelling, agglomeration only
signifies competitive inefficiencies and decreased social welfare.

With a more elastic demand curve, firms will be less prone to
agglomerate at the median location since it will lose customers
at the furthest end of the market.[6] Thus, the tendency to
agglomerate will decline as the elasticity of demand increases.
This point is illustrated in Figure 3.3. In this example, we
assume that every consumer has an identical demand curve. The
price intercept indicates the maximum delivered price that the
firm can charge since above this point, the quantity demanded
will be reduced to zero. The top half of the diagram depicts
Hotelling's agglomeration equilibrium. XY represents the length
of the market that the two firms attempt to supply. AB and CD
represent their respective processing costs. BF, BE, DE, and DG
indicate both firms' delivered price at each point in the market.

It is clear from this diagram that agglomeration is undesirable. Although both firms could divide the market evenly by
locating at the center, the pattern of delivered prices prevents
this outcome, since at the middle neither firm can supply its full
share of the market. Beyond point H and I, in other words, the
delivered price will exceed the price intercept on the demand
curve and demand will disappear. In this situation, new firms
located at the ends of the market can appear, and increase the
regional competition. However, by shifting to a more dispersed
pattern, although not necessarily to the socially optimum quartile location, both undesirable situations can be avoided. Each
firm will now span its entire allotted portion of the market and
since there are no longer any unsupplied consumers, new firms
will be discouraged from entering the region. Moreover, as the
elasticity of demand increases, the demand curve becomes hori-

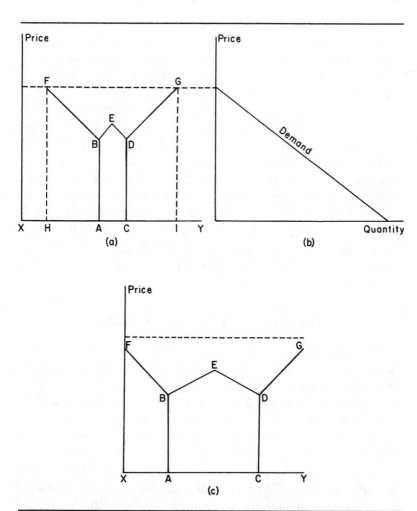

Figure 3.3: Demand Elasticity and Spatial Concentration

zontal and the y intercept decreases. Consequently, if the firms still wish to supply the entire market and eliminate new entrants, they will have to relocate once again by moving closer to the quartile positions. In the limiting case of a perfectly elastic demand curve, the only feasible location is at the quartiles.

Two additional points of clarification are necessary before the discussion of locational interdependence can be concluded. First, irrespective of the consumer's elasticity of demand, a quartile solution will always be socially optimal. *Relatively inelastic demand curves only permit suboptimal solutions; they are never a theoretically desirable state of affairs.* Only uncertainty and competition induce firms to locate at the socially suboptimal median. Second, elastic demand curves will not force competing firms to adopt quartile locations if transportation charges are relatively minimal. In this case, goods can be hauled long distances without producing any adverse effects on delivered prices and demand. Therefore, within the context of locational interdependence theory we can state that the higher the transport charges, the greater the dispersion of industry. As transport rates fall, the tendency for agglomeration will increase.

SPATIAL PRICE DISCRIMINATION

The previous section demonstrated that with realistic assumptions about demand elasticity, agglomeration was theoretically impossible as well as socially undesirable. Yet despite its impossibility, concentrated industrial belts have developed and firms have found it both possible and profitable to supply the national market from one production site. The reduction in freight rates is one factor that could permit agglomeration. Localization and urbanization economies are another. Unfortunately, by themselves, the secular decline in freight rates and agglomeration economies do not account for all the factors influencing regional development patterns. Specifically, past legal decisions sanctioning and prohibiting various forms of spatial price discrimination have also played a major part in the regional dispersion and concentration of industry. According to one economist, these "decisions are landmarks in an effort to preserve a free market in the United States and to give the outlying communities of America a fair chance to participate in our country's economic development."[7] Therefore, a complete discussion of location theory and regional development must include an analysis of spatial pricing policies. Consequently, this section will discuss the theory of spatial price discrimination while the following section will analyze the influence of one form of price discrimination—basing points—on the industrial development of the Sunbelt.

Spatial price discrimination can take two forms—discrimination against the distant customers and discrimination against the nearer customers. First we will consider the case in which the distant consumers are charged a price which exceeds factory costs plus transportation charges between the factory and the point of consumption. According to Hoover, the distant consumers will pay "phantom freight" when "all buyers have identical demand schedules, of constant as well as equal elasticity, at their respective locations. The elasticity of demand, e, is the same at every point of every buyer's curve."[8] If p is the delivered price paid by the consumer and t the transport charges for the commodity, then the firm's marginal revenue will be:

$$\frac{d(px)}{dx} - t = \frac{p \cdot dx + x \cdot dp}{dx} - t = p + \frac{xdp}{dx} - t.$$

But since elasticity, e, is equal to $\frac{p \circ dx}{x \circ dp}$, the expression for marginal revenue may be simplified to the following form:

$$p - \frac{p}{e} - t = p(\frac{e-1}{e}) - t.$$

The price paid by any buyer at a particular distance from the city is found by equating marginal revenue with marginal cost, c, and then solving for p. When these operations are completed, the price paid by the buyer at his location is equal to $\frac{e(c+t)}{e-1}$

The price received by the seller at the seller's location is equal to the delivered price minus transport charges or p− t, which, in turn, may be expressed as:

$$\frac{e(c+t)}{e-1} - t = \frac{ec + t}{e - 1} .$$

Since this expression increases as t increases, the mill price paid by distant consumers is greater than the mill price paid by those consumers located adjacent to the firm. This signifies spatial price discrimination. However, as e increases, the ability to discriminate decreases and in the limiting case of infinite elasticity, price discrimination disappears.

However, in reality, the distant customers do not pay phantom freight. Instead, producers generally practice freight absorption by charging the distant consumers less than the mill price plus transportation. In other words, in order to extend the firm's market area, the firm gives the distant consumers a subsidy in the form of reduced freight costs.

There are several possible explanations for this behavior. First, a firm can increase its sales and invade the natural market area of a competitor either by lowering its mill price to all consumers including those in the firm's natural market area or by absorbing freight and reducing its marginal revenue only on sales to the newly acquired, distant consumers.[9] Since the latter practice produces a smaller reduction in total revenue, from the firm's perspective, it is clearly the most desirable alternative.

Second, Hoover's initial analysis assumes that buyers' demand curves all have constant and equal elasticities. Yet as Hoover himself points out, this is an unrealistic assumption. When the more remote buyers have a more elastic demand, then it will not be feasible to gain sales in the distant regions by charging these consumers a higher mill price. In fact, with a highly elastic demand in the remote areas, total revenue can be increased by reducing prices rather than by raising prices. Also, it is unrealistic to postulate only constant elasticity demand curves. With straight line demand curves, elasticity decreases as the price falls. Under these circumstances it will be most profitable to discriminate against nearer buyers.

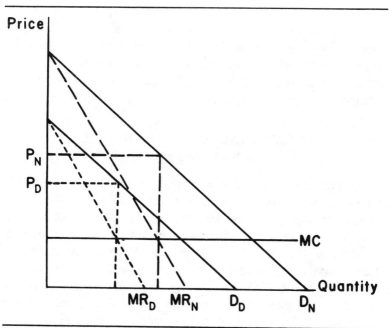

Figure 3.4: Price Discrimination Against Proximate Consumers

Figure 3.4 presents the demand and marginal revenue curves *as the seller sees them* for two buyers who are identical in all respects except distance between the buyer and the point of production. As a result of this distance differential, the demand curve (which represents delivered price minus transport charges) and marginal revenue line of the distant buyer will shift down by an amount equal to transport costs. The profit maximizing entrepreneur will charge consumers in each distance zone a price that is determined by equating the firm's marginal cost and marginal revenue. As the diagram clearly shows, this results in a lower mill price for the distant buyer.

Finally, businessmen discriminate against the more proximate consumers because evasion is more difficult. With discrimination against distant buyers, evasion is simple. Instead of buying direct from the factory and paying phantom freight, the distant consumers can purchase from closer consumers and only pay the freight charge from the resale point to the final destination.

The opposite form of discrimination is impossible to evade unless the seller is absorbing the entire freight cost. With any lesser amount of freight absorption, spatial arbitrage does not work since the distant buyers will not be able to act as purchasing agents and undersell the delivered price charged by the factory to the proximate consumers.

LOCATIONAL INTERDEPENDENCE: BASING POINT PRICING

The preceding three sections added demand considerations to the list of variables influencing industrial location. Within the context of that discussion we illustrated the impact of regional price differentials on the size and shape of a firm's market area. In addition, the section on spatial price discrimination demonstrated that businessmen do not have to adhere to a uniform F.O.B. pricing system. Instead, by imposing price discrimination, they can expand their market area and raise their profits without lowering prices in their natural market. Finally, the section on location interdependence discussed the forces promoting industrial concentration and dispersion. In that section we demonstrated that although industrial dispersion was socially optimal, it would be rarely achieved in a competitive environment.

Now that these three factors have been discussed, we can link them to an analysis of regional development. Specifically we will focus upon one method of spatial price discrimination, basing point pricing, in order to understand how this system has influenced the regional patterns of industrial location. The development of this section will proceed in three stages: (1) a description of the basing point method of price quotation; (2) a comparison of basing point pricing and F.O.B. pricing; and (3) a discussion of the impact of basing points on regional development.

Basing Point Pricing

The evolution of basing point prices is most prominently associated with the steel and cement industries although its use has not been confined solely to these two branches of manu-facturing.[10] This method of price quotation designates one plant or region as a basing point for a certain commodity. Delivered prices to any consuming point are computed by adding the mill price of the base plant plus transportation charges from the basing point to the point of consumption. Generally all transport rates are quoted as if the commodity had been shipped by rail even though cheaper forms of transportation may have been used. This formula is employed by all production facilities in all locations despite any variations in processing costs at the different locations and any differentials in actual transport charges. As a result of this system, every consumer pays the same delivered price irrespective of the location and costs of the firm from which he purchases. Delivered prices of all plants, therefore, are governed solely by the price at the basing point and transportation charges from the basing point.[11]

Freight absorption and phantom freight are inherent features of basing point pricing. For example, the steel industry originally established one basing point in Pittsburgh even though steel production occurred in the Chicago-Gary District and in Birmingham, Alabama. However, with basing point pricing, steel producers in Chicago who were selling in Chicago had to charge their customers a delivered price that was identical to the delivered price that would have been charged had the steel been purchased in Pittsburgh and delivered to Chicago. Since this price included freight charges between Pittsburgh and Chicago, the Chicago producers were forced to include phantom freight in their price quotations. However, if Chicago steel mills sold in the Pittsburgh region, they had to absorb freight costs since the delivered price of steel in Pittsburgh did not include any freight charges.

Both the Chicago and Pittsburgh steel producers profited from this system, although ultimately the major advantage rested with the Pittsburgh producers. Due to the phantom freight they collected on sales within their natural market area, Chicago producers realized a higher "mill net" than would have been possible without the basing point system. However, this advantage was offset by freight absorption on sales beyond their natural market area. Pittsburgh steel producers, on the other hand, could not charge phantom freight but this disadvantage was offset by the knowledge that the Pittsburgh plus system ensured Pittsburgh steel producers equal access to every consuming center in the nation.

Five qualities characterize industries that establish a basing point method of price quotation:[12]

(1) They produce homogeneous products. Therefore, consumers will purchase from the firm that offers the lowest delivered price.

(2) Production is localized in a few, widely scattered centers.

(3) Fixed costs are a major component of total costs. As a result, economies of scale exist over a wide range of output and marginal costs are below average costs. The difference between marginal cost and average cost signifies the permissible amount of freight absorption. Although in the long run the "mill net" must equal the average cost, any sales that produce a mill net in excess of marginal cost will be desirable even if they require freight absorption. By selling the marginal unit, average costs decline and any surplus above the marginal cost can be applied to the fixed cost. Therefore, as a result of this cost structure, every firm desires to absorb freight charges and increase sales by raiding another firm's market area.

(4) Transportation costs are substantial but they do not create impenetrable barriers between regions.

(5) There is a geographically unstable demand for the product. While demand in one region booms, it slumps someplace else. Firms facing this pattern of boom and bust cannot survive if they sell only in their natural market area. With a slump in demand, average costs increase and firms must raise prices. Rather than respond in this perverse fashion, they utilize freight absorption to gain customers outside their natural market area.[13]

Basing Points vs. F.O.B. Pricing

At first it would appear that basing point pricing offers a rational solution to a unique situation. Through freight absorption, firms maintain a high level of production despite regional fluctuations in demand. This reduces average costs. Also, by concentrating industrial facilities in a few locations, each unit has a large market and an opportunity to achieve economies of scale. This, too, reduces average costs and if these savings are sufficiently large, they may offset the loss resulting from freight absorption. Moreover, freight absorption promotes competition and therefore should not have been declared a violation of the antitrust laws. With basing point pricing every producer has access to more than one market and consequently, no firm can establish a spatial monopoly. An F.O.B. pricing system, by comparison, assigns every producer to a separate region. Although the extent of the market area is governed by the prices set in the adjacent regions, within its natural market every producer is a monopolist. Therefore, some have argued that nondiscriminatory F.O.B. price systems are monopolistic but basing points are competitive.[14]

Fetter, however, disagrees with this assessment. In his opinion, basing points are a clear example of monopolistic collusion while F.O.B. prices represent the epitome of competitive behavior.[15] Among his reasons for favoring F.O.B. pricing are:

(1) With F.O.B. pricing, all buyers pay the same mill price and spatial differentials in delivered prices only result from transport cost variations. With freight absorption and phantom freight, the mill net varies according to the consumer's location and demand elasticity.

(2) With F.O.B. pricing, the delivered price at a specific destination varies with the firm's location. Under a basing point system all factories charge the same delivered price.

(3) Each F.O.B. production center can influence the size of its market area by raising or lowering its mill price according to the dictates of supply and demand. As a result, mill prices will change more frequently with F.O.B. pricing than with basing point pricing.[16]

(4) Freight absorption allows the financially strong corporations to engage in predatory pricing. In a nondiscriminatory pricing system this would be impossible.

(5) Under the regime of basing points buyers have no price incentive to change suppliers. However, F.O.B. pricing induces price competition and provides the consumer with a choice of suppliers.

(6) In an F.O.B. system, price changes affect a firm's market area and limit its monopoly power. In a basing point system, price increases at the base factory do not affect relative market areas.

(7) F.O.B. factories eliminate excess capacity by reducing prices and increasing market areas. Basing point factories, however, do not lower prices at every destination. Instead they maintain prices in some areas and absorb freight in others.

(8) F.O.B. mills permit the buyer to select the cheapest mode of transportation. Basing mills charge rail rates even when the product is shipped by some cheaper mode.

(9) Freight absorption leads to wasteful and inefficient cross-hauling. F.O.B. pricing eliminates this practice since each firm has a unique market area.

(10) F.O.B. pricing permits high-cost producers to locate and compete in those markets with the highest delivered prices. These high-cost firms can be eliminated only if other firms reduce their mill prices. With freight absorption, predatory pricing can be instituted solely to eliminate unwanted, weak competitors.

(11) Since F.O.B. pricing establishes a unique market area for each production center, the attempt to minimize delivered prices and maximize demand produces a socially optimal pattern of industrial dispersion. Basing point prices, by comparison, induce concentration at the basing point and distort the site selection process.

Basing Points and Regional Prosperity

Fetter's last objection suggests that when compared to a basing point, nonbase locations represent inferior high-cost sites for both producers and consumers. Because of this inferiority, capacity adjustments will not reflect regional shifts in demand. Since nonbase mills collect phantom freight on all sales within their natural market, their profit margins become inflated artificially. This reduces the speed with which excess capacity disappears from nonbase locations. More ominously, firms located at basing points can shift the excess capacity to nonbase factories. As demand falls at the basing point factories, their incentives to invade the market area of other production centers increases. Since the base mills encounter no delivered price disadvantages on sales to remote areas, these incursions pose few problems for them. "Thus, in the special circumstances in which the home market of the base mill is the region of the greatest decline in demand, the single basing point system would lead to a slower reduction in capacity."[17]

When regional demand increases at different rates, the basing point system distorts the location of new facilities. With F.O.B. pricing, the region with the most rapid demand increase will receive new production capacity as soon as the market can support an additional unit. But with basing points, if the new demand appears at a nonbase location, the threat of market penetration from the basing point will inhibit entrepreneurs in the rapidly growing region from constructing additional capacity. Constructing the new facility and retaliating by invading the market area of the base point is also impossible since plants located at a nonbase location must absorb freight. As a result, basing points concentrate productive capacity in the base region and discourage the growth of nonbase regions. These tendencies exist even when demand declines in the base region and increases in the nonbase region.

Because they distort industrial location, basing points had a detrimental influence on Sunbelt development. In 1939, for example, Birmingham steel mills had a cost advantage that ranged from $2.70 to $5.56 per ton. In Birmingham, the total cost of materials and labor was $11.63 per ton. In Pennsylvania, it was $17.05 and in Indiana, $14.82. Birmingham's natural market area included Texas, Oklahoma, Arkansas, Louisiana, Mississippi, Alabama, Tennessee, North Carolina, South Carolina, Georgia, and Florida.[18] However, basing point pricing constricted Birmingham's natural market. Stocking estimates that, as a result of this system,

> Birmingham mills supplied only 309 tons or 36.1 percent of the area's total requirement. They supplied no Texas buyers with drawn wire, although Texas bought more of it than any other state in Birmingham's natural market. Texans bought their wire largely from Pittsburgh, Sparrows Point, Maryland, and Pueblo, Colorado. Louisiana customers bought 129 tons of plain drawn wire but they bought only five tons, or less than four percent of their requirements, from

Birmingham mills. Had Birmingham mills supplied all customer requirements in their natural market, and no customers elsewhere, they could have sold more than two and one-half times as much wire as they in fact sold.[19]

Besides reducing Birmingham's market area, basing point pricing discouraged steel consumers from locating near Birmingham and encouraged them to choose a site near one of the basing points. By locating at a base point, phantom freight on steel shipments can be eliminated. At nonbase locations, the delivered price includes frieght charges even though the steel was purchased from a nearby mill. As a result, fabricators at nonbase locations face a competitive disadvantage that artificially reduces their market area.[20] Since most basing points were in the northeast, steel fabricators chose to locate there instead of near the lower-cost Birmingham steel mills.

CENTRAL PLACE THEORY

In many respects, central place theory resembles market area analysis. Both deal with the location of industry and both assume that delivered prices promote spatial regularities. However, despite these similarities, the differences between the two warrants a separate analysis of central place theory. Therefore, this section will discuss the mechanics of central place theory. However, this discussion will not delve into all the nuances and mathematical complexities that traditionally have been associated with central place theory.[21] Instead it will highlight only those aspects that analyze the uneven spatial distribution of economic activity.

Market area analysis studies the spatial distribution of several firms within an industry. The quest to maximize total revenue within the context of either a dispersed or concentrated spatial arrangement forms the core of the inquiry. Central place theory expands this analysis in several directions. First, it arranges activities along a hierarchical continuum and then determines the optimal location for the entire complement of activities.

Second, central place theory emphasizes the distribution of cities and not the location of a particular industry. It assumes that some cities, or central places, contain a wide variety of activities including many higher-order industries while other central places possess only a few lower-order industries. As a result, the larger central places occur less frequently while the smaller central places are dispersed throughout the region. This distribution of hierarchically ordered central places promotes uneven, although uniformly patterned, development.

Unfortunately, while central place theory adds many important insights to market area analysis, its abstract formulation limits its historical relevance. Therefore, one of its most ardent adherents calls central place theory "a purely deductive theory" composed of "logical constructs in search of a test."[2][2] Nevertheless, despite its abstract formulation, it deserves careful consideration because it is the first theory to emphasize the economic forces producing a system of cities.

Central place theory assumes a set of initial conditions that resemble Von Thunen's isolated state. But there is one major difference. Von Thunen's isolated state contained only one city surrounded by a vast agricultural hinterland. Central place theory posits a region filled with numerous central places that supply central goods and services to their hinterland. Examples of central goods are gasoline stations, retail establishments, personal services, schools, churches, radio and television stations, health services, legal advice, financial services, and entertainment.

These central goods and services are arrayed hierarchically on the basis of market areas or "the range of a good." Central place theorists employ two concepts to develop this hierarchy. The threshold population "is the minimum population size of an urban center for the support of an urban function."[2][3] It measures the critical level of demand needed to capture the necessary scale economies and remain in business. When coupled with population density data, the threshold population indicates the maximum feasible industrial dispersion consistent with "normal profits." The "range of a good" measures the

maximum distance between production centers that will provide every consumer access to every commodity. The range can
be defined by two criteria. The ideal limit is the maximum
distance that a consumer will travel to purchase a commodity.
Beyond this distance, the high delivered price will choke off all
demand. Consequently, as in market area analysis, the ideal
limit provides an index of the maximum agglomeration or
minimum dispersion consistent with supplying the most distant
consumers. Together, the ideal limit and threshold population
establish the upper and lower bounds of agglomeration. The
"real limit" lies somewhere between the ideal limit and the
threshold population. It measures the actual extent of a firm's
market area and reflects the current and possibly nonoptimal
distribution of activities.

Since different activities have different threshold levels and
ideal limits, they will not be dispersed equally throughout a
region. Those with higher threshold levels will be found only in
the larger, more centrally located, higher order urban centers.
Similarly, low threshold activities will spread more uniformly
throughout the region and they will locate in smaller urban
centers. Two major conclusions concerning the growth of cities
and the interrelationship between various members of the system of cities flow from this simple observation.

First, Berry and Garrison[24] discovered that the best equation
for estimating the population of a central place was $P=A(B)^N$
where:

P = population of a center
N = number of stores located in a center
A = estimated threshold population
B = coefficient of economies of scale

Suppose that the threshold population for one unit of a particular central good is 1000. Based on their equation, two units will
not appear when the population exceeds 2000. If the estimated
value of B is 4, the second unit will appear only after the
population exceeds $1000(4)^2$, or 16,000. In other words, the

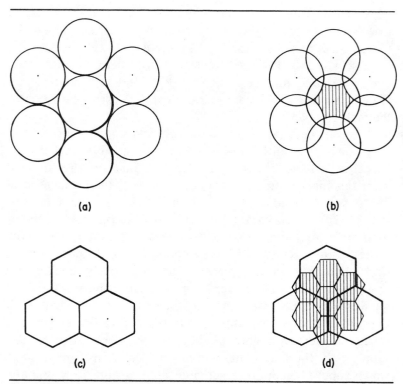

(a) (b) (c) (d)

Figure 3.5: Classical Central Place Theory

appearance of a second unit is not an additive process. Instead, the existence of economies of scale requires exponential population growth before a second unit can succeed in a city.

Second, urban centers can be arrayed along a hierarchical continuum that reflects the economic relationships among various members of the system of cities. Christaller offers one explanation for the evolution of this urban hierarchy. He begins by ranking central goods and services according to the population threshold. Then he assumes that a large city located at the center of the region supplies the full complement of central goods and services. In the absence of competing centers, its market area will be a circle with a radius equal to the largest ideal limit of all the goods supplied by that city. However, the presence of competing centers alters the size and shape of the town's market area. Since every consumer must be supplied by at least one center, nonoverlapping circular market areas cannot exist (Figure 3.5, Panel A). Instead, Christaller postulates overlapping circular market areas (Panel B) that became hexagons (Panel C) owing to the competition within the shared portion of the market area.

However, because of its extensive market area, the town can only supply the entire region with those goods that have the largest ideal limit. The remaining central goods are also supplied from this highest order center but because of their smaller ideal limits, some portions of the region will not have a source of supply. This creates an opportunity for a second tier of towns to supply everything offered by the largest center except the highest order service. By continuing this line of reasoning, Christaller deduces the presence of successively smaller and more numerous centers supplying only successively lower-level services. The final result is a complete system of cities with each tier distributed evenly throughout the region (Panel D). The smaller centers are more ubiquitous and, consequently, they supply only those activities with a low ideal limit. Large centers which supply higher-order activities are less numerous, and as a result, higher order activities are less dispersed. With this deduced pattern of nested market areas, Christaller believes he has explained both the uneven distribution of activities as well as the economic linkages uniting various levels of the urban hierarchy.

Unfortunately, Christaller's model does not offer a realistic analysis of either urban industrial structure or the process of urban growth. In his system, all cities on the same level of the urban hierarchy supply identical items to their hinterland. A city that is on the next higher level contains all the activities found in the lower level centers plus one or two additional functions located only at this or higher levels. Similarly, as we descend the hierarchy, cities shed the higher-order activities but retain the lower-level functions. Size, in other words, becomes a perfect predictor of a city's industrial structure. In addition, since the only difference between large cities and small cities is the presence of higher-order activities, Christaller's model suggests that cities grow by adding activities with higher ideal limits. Growth, therefore, becomes an incremental, additive process that does not effect the preceding economic foundation.

Losch's model of the central place system departs from Christaller's in several important respects. First, the Loschian system is not limited to the distribution of services. Instead, it includes and ranks all activities along a hierarchical continuum. In addition, within the Loschian model, it is perfectly acceptable for two cities on the same hierarchical level to have totally different industrial structures. But in the process of correcting some of the defects of Christaller's formulation, Losch converts urban growth into an ahistorical, stochastic process that bears little resemblance to actual evolution of the urban system.

Figure 3.6 presents the essential features of Losch's central place scheme. It assumes that the city supplies a variety of central goods and services to its surrounding hinterland and that each commodity has a different threshold population. What will be the resulting spatial configuration of economic activity? Since product 1 has the smallest threshold level, it will appear in every center. Product 2, however, requires a larger market and, consequently, it is found in every other city. Product 3, with a still larger threshold requirement, will be located in every third city. By continuing this process, Losch finds an appropriate location for every industry.

Having deduced the spatial configuration, Losch proceeds to relate this to urban size. He assumes that a city's population is proportional to the size of its industries where size is computed by summing the rank of every industry located in that city. Panel B presents the resulting relative size distribution for the urban system. City A contains all seven activities and its population is 28. City M, the next largest center, does not produce a full complement of commodities. Product 7 is missing and its absence conforms to Christaller's assertion that the second tier of cities will produce everything but the highest-order activity.

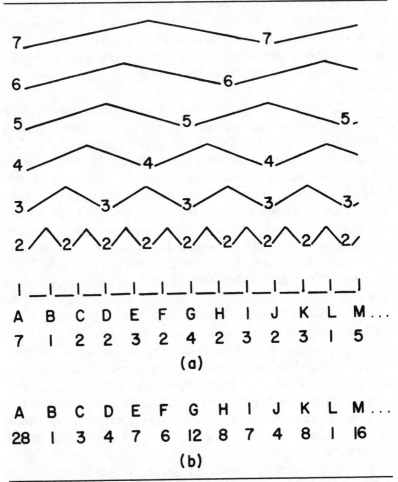

Figure 3.6: An Alternative Model of Central Place Theory

However, in addition, product 5 is missing and this violates Christaller's theory. Therefore, in the Loschian world, lower-order cities need not replicate the lower-order portion of the industrial structure of higher-order cities. As a result, a city's position in the urban hierarchy cannot predict the industries found in that city. Moreover, towns of the same size do not necessarily produce the same goods. This can be seen by comparing the industrial structure of City H and City K. Finally, unlike Christaller's scheme, large-scale industry does not have to congregate in the largest towns. Small centers can provide equally suitable environments. They are small only because they have failed to attract more than one or two industries. City size is not influenced by the type of industry that has been attracted.

NOTES

1. Much of this discussion is derived from Melvin Greenhut, *Plant Location in Theory and Practice* (Chapel Hill: Univ. of North Carolina Press, 1954): 25-37; and also from Frank A. Fetter, "The Economic Law of Market Areas," *Quarterly Journal of Economics* 38, 4 (1924): 520-529.

2. Fetter, op. cit.: 521.

3. Harold Hotelling, "Stability In Competition," *Economic Journal* 39 (March 1929): 53.

4. Fetter, op. cit.: 527.

5. Hotelling, op. cit.

6. On this point, see Arthur F. Smithies, "Optimum Location in Spatial Competition," *Journal of Political Economy* 49, 3 (1941): 423-439; and also Morris A. Copeland, "Competing Products and Monopolistic Competition," *Quarterly Journal of Economics* 55, 1 (1940-1941): 1-35.

7. Corwin D. Edwards, "The Effects of Recent Basing Point Decisions upon Business Practices," *American Economic Review* 38, 5 (1948): 829.

8. Edgar M. Hoover, "Spatial Price Discrimination," *Review of Economic Studies* 4, 3 (1935): 184.

9. For a discussion of the optimal amount of freight absorption, see Greenhut, op. cit.: 44-57; and George Stigler, "A Theory of Delivered Price Systems," *American Economic Review* 39, 6 (1949): 1143-1159.

10. See Edwards, op. cit., for examples of other industries that have utilized basing point pricing formulae.

11. Descriptions of the mechanics of basing point pricing can be found in Arthur Smithies, "Aspects of the Basing Point System," *American Economic Review* 32, 4 (1942): 705-725; J. M. Clark, "Basing Point Methods of Price Quotation," *Canadian Journal of Economics and Political Science* 4, 4 (1938): 477-489; Donald Dewey, "A Reappraisal of F.O.B. Pricing and Freight Absorption," *Southern Economic Journal* 22, 1 (1955): 48-54; Carl Kaysen, "Basing Point Pricing and Public Policy," *Quarterly Journal of Economics* 63, 3 (1949): 289-314; Fritz Machlup, *The Basing Point System* (Philadelphia: Blakiston Co., 1949): 25-30; and George W. Stocking, *Basing Point Pricing and Regional Development* (Chapel Hill: Univ. of North Carolina Press, 1954): Chapter 1.

12. These characteristics are described in Clark, op. cit.: 477-478.

13. This last point was not included in Clark's list of characteristics but it is emphasized strongly by Stigler, op. cit.

14. For a full discussion of these arguments, see Frank A. Fetter, "The New Plea for Basing Point Monopoly," *Journal of Political Economy* 45, 5 (1937): 577-605.

15. Frank Fetter, "Exit Basing Point Pricing," *American Economic Review* 38, 5 (1948): 815-827.

16. Kaysen, however, disagrees with this assertion. "It seems doubtful that uniform F.O.B. mill pricing would produce any better results from the point of view of price flexibility than a universal freight equalization system, and it may even produce somewhat inferior ones" (Kaysen, op. cit.: 296). His argument is based on the oligopolistic nature of basing point industries which ensures that all firms will recognize the futility of price cutting as a device to increase market shares. Also, Clark writes, "It is not certain whether in the long run, it [F.O.B. pricing] would increase the strength of competitive pressures on prices or reduce it" (Clark, op. cit.: 486).

17. Kaysen, op. cit.: 302.

18. Stocking, op. cit.: 83.

19. Ibid.: 89.

20. Kaysen, op. cit.: 304-305. Also see Corwin D. Edwards, "Geographic Price Formulas and the Concentration of Economic Power," *Georgetown Law Journal* 37, 1 (1949): 135-148; and William Summers Johnson, "The Restricted Incidence of Basing Point Pricing on Regional Development," *Georgetown Law Journal* 37, 1 (1949): 149-165.

21. A complete mathematical treatment of central place theory can be found in August Losch, *The Economics of Location* (New Haven, CT: Yale Univ. Press, 1954): part II; Walter Christaller, *The Central Places of Southern Germany* (Englewood Cliffs, NJ: Prentice-Hall, 1966); Brian Berry, *Geography of Market Centers and Retail Distribution* (Englewood Cliffs, NJ: Prentice-Hall, 1967): Chapter 4. A complete bibliography of central place studies has been compiled by Brian Berry and Allan Pred, *Central Place Studies: A Bibliography of Theory and Applications* (Philadelphia: Regional Science Research Institute, 1965).

22. Brian Berry, "Cities as Systems Within Systems of Cities," *Papers and Proceedings of the Regional Science Association* 13 (1962): 147.

23. Brian Berry and W. L. Garrison, "A Note on Central Place Theory and the Range of a Good," *Economic Geography* 34, 4 (1958): 306. Also see Wolfgang Stolper, "Spatial Order and the Economic Growth of Cities," *Economic Development and Cultural Change* 3, 2 (1955): 137-147.

24. Berry and Garrison, op. cit.: 309.

Chapter 4

BASIC VERSUS NONBASIC INDUSTRIES

Up to this point, the analysis of uneven development has assumed that every industry promotes urban growth. Therefore, the analysis has been confined to the forces creating agglomeration and diffusion. Unfortunately, uneven development is not a static concept. While agglomeration and diffusion are part of this phenomenon, a complete discussion of uneven development must explain why *growth-inducing* activities agglomerate in certain regions and not in others. At best, location theory only provides half of the required explanation. To develop the remaining portions, we must separate the growth-inducing activities from those that are merely passive or reactive participants.

The basic vs. nonbasic analysis attempts to fill this gap by distinguishing between city-building (basic) activities and city-serving (nonbasic) activities.[1] It postulates that export or basic activities provide an exogenous source of new income for a city. Since these basic industries require support services, their growth stimulates growth in the city serving or nonbasic segment of the local economy. As a result, only growth in the export sector affects the prosperity of the local economy. Since expansion in the nonbasic portion is merely a passive response to stimuli emitted by the basic sector, it cannot initiate additional rounds of urban development. This chapter will examine the merits of this theoretical distinction. Two lines of inquiry will be pursued—the measurement of the economic base and the importance of basic industries to a city's growth and prosperity.

THE MEASUREMENT OF THE ECONOMIC BASE

The most precise method of identifying export activities is to survey every establishment and determine the volume of sales to outside consumers. However, except for small cities, this approach is too time consuming and complicated. Therefore, several short-cut methods have been suggested.

Location quotients compare national and local patterns of economic activity and indicate "the importance of the industry to the locality relative to the importance of the industry to the nation."[2] A location quotient is defined as the percentage of local employment in a particular industry divided by the percentage of national employment in that same industry. Mathematically it is expressed by the formula $\frac{e_i}{e_t} \Big/ \frac{E_i}{E_t}$ where:

e_i = local employment in industry i
e_t = total employment in the city
E_i = national employment in industry i
E_t = total national employment.

If the location quotient exceeds one, the city produces a surplus destined for the export market. A value equal to one implies local self-sufficiency, and a value less than one indicates a local deficit and the need for imports. Thus, any industry whose location quotient exceeds one is part of the economic base while the remainder are relegated to the nonbasic category.

Unfortunately, this technique requires several tenuous assumptions. Since the coefficients are based on employment figures, they only express the degree of labor force specialization in a locality. To infer that a city is a net exporter or net importer of a specific commodity, the analyst must assume that differences in labor productivity are negligible and that labor force specialization reflects product specialization. Without this assumption, location quotients might indicate that the city is a net exporter when in reality it is not even self-sufficient.

In addition, location quotients assume that every city's nonbasic economic structure replicates the benchmark economy. When the benchmark is a small region, this assumption, while still not necessarily valid, is not too unrealistic. Cities in the same region generally have similar factor endowments, disparities in processing costs are probably small, and access to markets is relatively equal. Under these circumstances, deviations from the average industrial structure should indicate a city's relative specialization and propensity to export. But, when the benchmark economy is the United States, these conditions no longer exist. Cities in regions that developed during different eras may be qualitatively dissimilar. With a different history and economic base, the necessary support services may also vary. Therefore, deviations from the average U.S. industrial structure may not imply the existence of an exportable surplus.

Also, the analysis assumes that demand is the same in every region. With this condition, location quotients that exceed one imply that excess production is destined for the export market. Without this condition, it is impossible to determine whether or not the industrial output will be consumed locally. For example, Houstonians rely on automobiles more than New Yorkers. Therefore, we would expect that Houston would need more automotive services than New York and that this would be reflected in a higher location quotient. Consequently, although Houston's location quotient may exceed one, this does not imply that excess production has occurred. It simply reflects the difference in demand for automotive services between Houston and the rest of the United States.[3]

Because of these objections, Mattila and Thompson believe that location quotients underestimate the measurement of a city's basic activities. To remedy this defect, they construct an absolute index of surplus workers equal to $e_i-(e_t/E_t) E_i$. In essence, their distinction between a location quotient and the index of surplus workers rests on the interpretation of basicness. With location quotients, an industry's basicness increases as the *proportion* of surplus workers increases. With their index of surplus workers, however, an industry's basicness increases as the *number* of surplus workers increases. This distinction is best illustrated by a hypothetical numerical example.

City A	Nation
$e_i = 20$	$E_i = 50$
$e_j = 40$	$E_j = 200$
$e_t = 100$	$E_t = 2000$
Industry "i"	Industry "j"
Location Quotient = 8.0	Location Quotient = 4.0
Surplus Workers = 17.5	Surplus Workers = 30

In this example, even though City A is more specialized in industry "i", it is clear that industry "j" contributes a greater number of surplus workers to the economic base. Therefore, "the index of surplus workers is a better measure of the net income generating capacity of a local industry and it would seem that this index exhibits a clear advantage over the index of local specialization as a measure of the 'basicness' of an industry to its locality."[4]

To obtain an even more precise measurement, they compute a relative index of surplus workers by dividing the surplus worker index by either total local employment or total surplus employment. Assume that we face the following situation:

	City A	City B
Surplus workers in industry "i"	20	
Surplus workers in industry "j"		15
Total surplus workers	40	20
Total employment	100	100

The total employment form of the relative surplus worker index has a value of .20 for City A. This exceeds the value in City B (.15). Yet the total surplus worker form shows that industry "i" in City A has a value of .50 while industry "j" in City B has a value of .75. Which industry is more basic? Even though both cities have the same total employment and despite the fact that the number of surplus workers in industry "i" exceeds the number of surplus workers in industry "j", City B will suffer more by the loss of industry "j". City A will lose a larger fraction of its total employment, but City B will lose a larger proportion of its economic base. Since it is the economic base that creates the prosperity of a city and induces changes in the size of the nonbasic component, the collapse of industry "j" in City B will destroy three-quarters of the basic economy, while the disappearance of industry "i" in City A will only destroy 50% of the basic economy.

The K value technique[5] and the minimum requirements[6] approach are two additional methods of estimating the economic base. Both assume that location quotients underestimate the volume of local exports and the size of a city's economic base. Several reasons for this underestimation were presented earlier, including the assumption of uniform demand and uniform productivity. In addition, location quotients measure surplus production by comparing a city's industrial structure with the national industrial structure. Unfortunately, the national

average includes production for average internal city requirements and average exports. Unless we eliminate average export
production from the national average industrial structure, it
becomes impossible to estimate accurately the economic base.
Both K values and minimum requirements are designed to solve
this problem.

Ullman and Dacey estimate the nonbasic component by
dividing urban areas into six size classifications. The largest size
category (over 1,000,000) contains fourteen cities while the
remaining categories contain thirty-eight cities selected at random. Then, for every city they compute the percentage of the
labor force employed in each of fourteen census categories
(agriculture, mining, construction, durable manufacturing, non-
durable manufacturing, transportation and communications,
wholesale trade, retail trade, finance and insurance, business and
repair services, personal services, entertainment, professional
services, and public administration). They designate the value
for the city with the minimum percentage employed in each
industry within each size category as the minimum requirement.
With this technique, they claim to identify the "empirical
minimum requirements for a viable city in the U.S. economy."[7] Finally, they sum the minima for each industry to
calculate the total percentage of *nonbasic* employment for each
size category. In 1950, they found that larger cities had a higher
proportion of nonbasic activities than smaller cities or, conversely, that smaller cities devoted a greater percentage of their
labor force to export functions than larger cities.

Alexandersson followed the same procedure but argued that
a minimum figure gave too much weight to cities with unusual
industrial structures. Consequently he arranged all 864 cities in
his sample by their percentage of employment in each industry
and chose the city at the fifth percentile as indicative of the
"necessary minimum to supply a city's own population with
goods and services of the type which are produced in every
normal city."[8] These minimum requirements were denoted as K
values.

Morrissett added an additional refinement to the K value technique. He computed the "employment-ratio" distribution of industries which he defined as "a distribution of the percentage of persons employed in a given industry in various cities of a given size."[9] K values only pinpoint the employment percentages for the fifth percentile of the employment ratio distribution. Morrissett's employment ratio technique examined all points on the distribution but placed special emphasis on the fifth percentile, the fiftieth percentile, and the ninetieth percentile. By examining the variations in these distributions by region and city size, he hoped to gain additional insight into the industrial structure of various cities and the forces promoting urban growth.

He discovered that on average, the dispersion between the ninetieth percentile and the K values was greater for small cities than for large cities. This implies that smaller cities are more dissimilar than large cities and that as cities grow, their industrial structures converge. Moreover, by examining the ninetieth percentile distribution he found that the specialized export-oriented economies are found in small, one industry towns. Larger cities, however, also contain export activities, but as the Loschian central place model showed, they are more diversified and devote a smaller proportion of their labor force to one single activity.

Based on his cross section analysis of cities during 1950, Morrissett proposed an evolutionary theory of urban growth. He claimed that if a city of 10,000 people is located on the fifth percentile of the employment ratio distribution, this city will remain on the fifth percentile line but as it grows, it resembles the structure of the larger, fifth percentile cities. In other words, cities grow by developing a more diversified industrial base and by reducing their reliance on a few specialized export activities.

Unfortunately, Morrissett's analysis and growth hypothesis contained several deficiencies. His theory of urban growth inferred dynamic processes from a cross-section study. Yet,

Morrissett never justified this methodology nor did he provide any empirical verification for his assertions. More importantly, the theory never explained how cities diversify. Do cities add basic or nonbasic industries? Do cities grow because they have added industries, or do they acquire new functions because they have grown? Do all cities at the fifth percentile point add the same functions to their industrial structure irrespective of the era during which they developed? Morrissett never attempted to answer any of these questions.

Finally, Morrissett argued that as cities grow, their industrial structures converge and obliterate most of the unique features that existed during their early stages. In other words, he assumed that the top of the urban hierarchy contains relatively homogeneous cities. When these large cities are compared with small towns and villages, their similarities are more striking than their differences. But does this mean that Houston, New York, and Cleveland contain the same industrial base? Unfortunately, Morrissett focused only on convergence and ignored the tendencies that produce dissimilarities in the upper ranks of the urban system.

THE DYNAMIC SIGNIFICANCE
OF THE ECONOMIC BASE

Despite the controversy surrounding the proper technique for estimating the urban base, several interesting points emerge from this literature. Practitioners of urban base analysis derive an urban multiplier by forming the ratio of nonbasic employment to basic employment. This multiplier has the misleading name of the "basic-nonbasic ratio." For example, if a city allocates one-third of its employment to basic industries and two-thirds to nonbasic industries, the multiplier is 2. This implies that adding one job in the basic sector creates two jobs in the nonbasic sector. With this technique, urban planners have assessed the impact of location decisions on the growth of the urban economy.

However, while the use of the multiplier may provide a rough estimate of induced growth, a blind application may convey a distorted impression of future growth prospects. Therefore, several intervening variables must be considered before the multiplier can be applied to a specific urban area.

For example, consider two cities with an identical distribution of employment between the basic and nonbasic sectors. We would expect that both cities would be equally affected by an equal increment of basic employment. However, if the two cities have unequal populations, this expectation would be wrong. Since the larger city surpassed many of the critical thresholds required to support a wide range of residentiary services, it will have a more complete array of nonbasic activities. Income earned from basic activities will remain within the local economy and boost the multiplier, while in the small, less developed city, leakages will increase and the multiplier will decrease.

Similarly, two cities that are identical in every respect except per capita income will not reap the same growth from equal increases in basic employment if the differences in wealth create disparities in the marginal propensity to consume local goods and services. Two effects will operate to reduce the multiplier in the wealthier community. In the first place, more spending will be devoted to luxuries supplied by other localities. This increases the leakages from the wealthier community. In the second place, the wealthier community might have a full complement of nonbasic services. As a result, the inducement to invest in local activities will be less. Therefore, in order to have the same growth rate, the wealthier city will need a larger dose of new basic employment.[10] Rapid growth, in other words, becomes progressively more difficult as a city becomes progressively more developed.

"Leverage effects" also influence the urban multiplier.[11] The concept of leverage is intimately related to the distinction between growth and development. Growth involves size and is concerned with *quantitative* variations. Development, however, deals with *qualitative* alterations. During the process of growth, size is the only variable that matters since everything retains its initial characteristics. A developmental process, on the other hand, involves more sweeping changes. Unfortunately, the urban multiplier only yields accurate predictions if the change is limited to growth. The multiplier is computed by observing a city's industrial structure at one point in time and therefore it is a static statistic that "assumes that as the city or region grows, the same profile will exist but made larger."[12] If we assume that development occurs, then the multiplier loses much of its utility. Several interacting factors alter the relationship between basic and nonbasic activities as a city develops. These factors have been termed leverage effects.

In the first place, it is essential to distinguish between the average basic-nonbasic ratio and the marginal ratio. Since the multiplier varies for cities with different populations, it is not possible to take the existing distribution of employment and assume that this ratio will reemerge after the basic sector has grown. With a larger population capable of supporting a wider variety of nonbasic services, the city's economy becomes more self-contained, leakages are reduced, and the multiplier increases. Therefore, with development, the marginal ratio is larger than the average ratio.

Second, unless an urban economy develops instantaneously, its industrial structure will contain different vintage activities. Therefore, even without any exogenous change, the local economy will be transformed through obsolescence and this will affect the basic-nonbasic ratio. When new basic activities are added to the shifting economic base, they generate new demands and stimulate changes in the composition of nonbasic activities. As a result, the historic ratio provides a poor basis for estimating the new multiplier.

In addition, the value of the multiplier depends upon the size of the area. A small city may export 50% of its production, a large city one-quarter, and the United States only one-twentieth. It does not follow, however, that if the United States were to double its exports, the national economy would expand by a factor of twenty. "What varies with the size of a region is the degree of self-sufficiency, not necessarily the leverage."[13]

This last point is of more than passing interest. It casts doubt upon the entire foundation of basic analysis. Urban base theorists argue that "insofar as role in a city's economic life is concerned, it is often more important to know whether an enterprise is basic or nonbasic than to know whether it is in manufacturing or trade."[14] North, for example, believes that exports are the major influence on a city's prosperity:

> Clearly, the export base plays a vital role in determining the level of absolute and per capita income of a region. While the return to factors of production in the export industries indicates the direct importance of these industries for the well being of the region, it is the indirect effect that is most important. Since residentiary industry depends entirely on demand with the region, it has historically been dependent on the fate of the export base.[15]

But are exports truly the fundamental determinant of urban growth? Is it true that residentiary activities are the passive element in a local economy? We can approach these questions from two perspectives.

On the one hand, we can distinguish between the long-run determinants of prosperity and the short-run influences. In the short run, exports affect the level of economic activity. Detroit, for instance, would be devastated if all the automobile plants were to curtail output. Similarly, steel in Pittsburgh and finance in New York are two other dominant exports whose health affects the prosperity of the local economy. But if we assume that a city's export base is transient and subject to constant alterations, then long-run prosperity does not depend upon a single export activity. Instead, with a basic sector that changes periodically, long-run local prosperity depends upon a city's ability to generate new basic activities.

What factors determine a locality's ability to attract new basic activities? Location theory suggests that regional disparities in processing costs are the dominant factor in location decisions. Especially important in this respect are agglomeration economies, and more specifically, urbanization economies. But a careful analysis of urbanization economies reveals that they are essentially residentiary, nonbasic services. In other words, in the long run a region's prosperity and ability to maintain a viable export base depend on the nonbasic services that it can offer prospective entrepreneurs. If this is true, then a city is branded by its residentiary industries and not by its export activities.[16]

In addition, other questions have been raised about the definition of basic activities and these suggest serious flaws in the relevance of the basic-nonbasic distinction. Blumenfeld argues that the entire discussion has been muddied by "mercantilistic and physiocratic overtones" that may no longer describe the reality of modern industrial and postindustrial urban life. With the rise of federal spending programs and other interregional wealth transfers (retirement cities or university towns, for example), "unearned" income, not exports, constitutes the major source of growth. Therefore, "the greater the amount of 'unearned' income flowing into or out of a community, the less applicable is the basic-nonbasic concept."[17]

Moreover, Blumenfeld argues that if basic activities are an indication of local prosperity, then we should focus less upon the physical movement of goods between cities and more on the region's balance of payments. If we approach the problem according to this perspective, serious revisions of the definition of basic activities are in order. For instance, consider a locality that was previously importing vast quantities of services and raw materials. With import substitution, these leakages from the local economy cease and the urban balance of payments improves. Yet, due to the poorly conceived notion of basic, city-building activities, these new activities would be classified as nonbasic, nongrowth-inducing industries. Clearly, though, the city is better off and in some sense more prosperous after import substitution. Basic analysis must begin to take this fact into consideration.

In a similar vein, the local industrial organization influences the measurement of basic activities. For example, if steel is produced in a vertically integrated plant, the entire value added is counted as basic. But with the same volume of output produced in separate, nonintegrated plants, only the final product is basic. Measuring basic activities on the basis of ownership patterns is a flawed procedure, but it does influence the volume of observed basic activities and the assessment of a city's prosperity.

NOTES

1. For a complete discussion of the urban base concept, see Harold M. Mayer, "Making a Living in Cities: The Urban Economic Base," *Journal of Geography* 68, 2 (1969): 70-87; John Alexander, "The Basic-Nonbasic Concept of Urban Economic Functions," *Economic Georgraphy* 30, 3 (1954): 246-261; and a series of articles by Richard B. Andrews appearing in *Land Economics*, Vol. 29-Vol. 31. At this point it should also be noted that there is a contradiction between central place theory and urban base theory. What is exported in central place theory are central goods and services. These are support functions for the surrounding region, and the greater the quantity supplied, the larger the city. In the basic-nonbasic discussion, these services are consumed locally. Since they are not exported, they cannot induce growth.

2. John M. Matilla and Wilbur Thompson, "The Measurement of the Economic Base of the Metropolitan Area," *Land Economics* 31, 3 (1955): 216.

3. For this reason, Hildebrand and Mace establish a cutoff point of 1.508 to distinguish between export and residentiary activities. Unfortunately, they offer no theoretical justification for their choice of a critical location quotient value. See George Hildebrand and Arthur Mace, "The Employment Multiplier in an Expanding Industrial Market: Los Angeles County, 1940-1947," *Review of Economics and Statistics* 32, 3 (1950): 246.

4. Matilla and Thompson, op. cit.: 220.

5. See Gunnar Alexandersson, *The Industrial Structure of American Cities* (Lincoln: Univ. of Nebraska Press, 1956); and Irving Morrissett, "The Economic Structure of American Cities," *Papers and Proceedings of the Regional Science Association* 4 (1957): 239-258.

6. Edward Ullman and Michael Dacey, "The Minimum Requirements Approach to the Urban Economic Base," *Papers and Proceedings of the Regional Science Association* 6 (1960): 175-199; Edward Ullman, Michael Dacey, and Joseph Brodsky,

The Economic Base of American Cities (Seattle: Univ. of Washington Center for Urban and Regional Research, 1969); and Edward Ullman, "Minimum Requirements after a Decade: A Critique and a Reappraisal," *Economic Geography* 44, 4 (1968): 364-369.

7. Ullman and Dacey, op. cit.: 177.

8. Alexandersson, op. cit.: 35.

9. Morrissett, op. cit.: 246.

10. See W. R. Pfouts and Earle Curtis, "Limitations of the Economic Base Analysis," *Social Forces* 36, 4 (1958): 303-310; and Charles Tiebout, "Community Income Multipliers: A Population Growth Model," *Journal of Regional Science* 2, 1 (1960): 75-84.

11. This discussion is abstracted from Charles T. Stewart, "Economic Base Dynamics," *Land Economics* 35, 4 (1959): 327-336.

12. Ibid.: 335.

13. Ibid.: 332.

14. Alexander, op. cit.: 255.

15. Douglas C. North, "Location Theory and Regional Economic Growth," *Journal of Political Economy* 63, 3 (1955): 248.

16. For a complete elaboration of this argument see Charles M. Tiebout, "Exports and Regional Economic Growth," *Journal of Political Economy* 64, 2 (1956): 160-164.

17. Hans Blumenfeld, "The Economic Base of the Metropolis," *Journal of the American Institute of Planners* 21 (Fall 1955): 117.

Chapter 5

DYNAMIC MODELS OF URBAN GROWTH

THE NEED FOR DYNAMIC THEORY

The previous chapters explored several theories that form the foundations of urban and regional growth analysis. Location theory, central place theory, and the basic-nonbasic distinction all provide insights and clues that illuminate some of the features associated with the regional redistribution of wealth and economic activity. Unfortunately, because they lack historical specificity and fail to explain urban growth within a context of general economic development, these theories offer only partial explanations of uneven development. They view cities as institutions that exist in a vacuum, unrelated to outside events or pressures and uninfluenced by changes within the broader economic system. As such, they are statements of the spatial conditions required for economic success, but they are not explanations of the process of economic development and spatial evolution.

Certainly, no industry can prosper if its location decision ignores raw materials, markets, and the presence of competing firms. In this context, location theory explains certain features of the economic landscape and provides insight into some of the forces that alter the spatial distribution of economic activity. Yet, despite these virtues, it is a limited tool for dynamic analysis. For example, location theory describes how certain variables attract industry to new metropolitan centers. But by confining the analysis to the realm of location theory, we are unable to determine whether the new location attracts only new activities and new industries or if many old activities also abandon their former location and migrate to the new region.

This question constitutes the core of urban growth analysis. It asks whether new cities are merely relocated carbon copies of their older counterparts or if they possess qualitatively different industrial structures. Moreover, it forces us to address the relationship between and desirability of urban growth in one region and urban decay someplace else. For instance, if new cities grow by cannibalizing the activities located in old cities, then the formation of new cities within the context of a preexisting urban system represents a zero sum game. Under these circumstances, we should seriously question the desirability of new cities. But if this is not a correct scenario, then location theory does not offer a complete analysis of urban dynamics. Since these questions cannot be answered within the static context of location theory, we must develop a theory that focuses explicitly on the dynamic interactions between cities.

Similar objections can be directed at the static analysis that characterizes the basic-nonbasic controversy. At no point in that debate do the authors distinguish between the export and residentiary industries found in old and new cities. Are they qualitatively different and at different stages in the product life cycle? Can these differences, if they do exist, explain the disparate growth trends in old and new cities? Unfortunately, this theoretical debate does not attempt to explain why declining cities cannot generate a new, dynamic export sector while rapidly growing cities seem to be relatively unaffected by this problem.

To answer these questions, we must develop a theory of urban dynamics that can build upon, but which is not limited to, the insights provided by the static, general equilibrium analysis discussed in the previous chapter. Only by viewing urbanization in the broader context of national and international economic development and identifying each city's role in this process can we begin to fill the gaps left by the more traditional analysis. Yet within the American context, very few theorists address these issues.

Most efforts to classify cities on the basis of their industrial structure represent unabashed exercises in taxonomy.[1] For example, one study that defined itself as a midcentury benchmark analysis of the current economic status of fifty major urban centers reported that their "analysis is almost wholly static or cross sectional; we are concerned with structure rather than dynamics."[2] In view of these structural and static studies, it is easy to sympathize with the lament of historians who declare that traditional urban economics does not

> formally confront the temporal problem of economic change and development. . . . At virtually no point in the burgeoning urban-regional literature, nor in the older stand of location analysis, do economists yet come to grips with the secular process of urbanization itself. . . . To be sure, urban-regional and location economists have not been concerned with the evolution of city systems as such nor with the analysis of long run economic transformations. However, were an investigator who was concerned with such phenomena to start from these two vantage points, he would shortly find himself proceeding under the severe constraints imposed by the ahistorical micro framework of the general theory of location.[3]

This chapter will explore some early theoretical efforts to address the deficiencies and limitations of traditional urban economic analysis. This literature can be divided into two major categories: (1) theories suggesting that cities pass through various stages as they ascend the urban hierarchy comprise one theoretical school; (2) the other approach emphasizes the differences between economic epochs and describes the influence of the mercantile and industrial eras on the type of economic activities that induce rapid urban growth.

THE STAGES OF GROWTH MODEL

Both Wilbur Thompson[4] and Jane Jacobs[5] present detailed models that serve as general theories of urban development. They both attribute the prosperity and dynamic qualities of an urban economy to the type of activities found in the city's industrial structure. For example, Thompson declares, "Tell me your industries and I will tell your (immediate) fortune. How could a highly specialized economy fail to reflect in its level, distribution, and stability of income and growth rates its distinctive industry mix?"[6] According to this theory, new industries, defined as those with high income elasticity and rapidly growing markets, ensure an adequate source of new income and guarantee local prosperity.

The Model in Brief

To start the analysis, Thompson assumes that one export activity locates in a city. Other firms in the same industry realize that this activity can prosper at this location, imitate the original entrepreneur's behavior, and also locate in the region. As a result, their joint location decision creates localization economies which strengthen the city's initial advantage. With an enlarged export sector, the area generates potential urbanization economies which attract firms that both supply the original export complex with needed materials and utilize its output. This increases the diversity of the city's industrial structure and serves two beneficial purposes: (1) If these new industries also develop into major exporters, the outside money entering the local economy will increase. According to the export base theorists, this improves the local business climate, creates a demand for additional nonbasic activities, and enlarges the local economy. (2) Previously, the materials and services provided by the new firms had been imported from other cities. Now, however, "import substitution" ends the "leakage of funds" to some other local economy. Thus, more money circulates through the city and less escapes to enrich a rival.

As the export sector grows, the demand for business services exceeds various critical thresholds and this permits greater local production and fewer imports. Again, leakages to rival centers decrease, and the volume of locally generated funds remaining within the urban economy increases. However, as the urban economy gains complexity through diversification, new demands arise for esoteric business services that the local economy cannot produce internally. Consequently, the positive effect of import substitution and export generation on the local balance of payments may be offset by new, additional imports. Yet an important developmental change has occurred. Simple exports and imports have been replaced by a more complex set of interurban transactions.

The expansion of the export and business service sectors creates new jobs and induces migration into the city. These two events also propel the local economy to greater levels of prosperity. Just as an increased demand for business services allowed the local economy to surpass critical threshold levels for business services, the increased population of the city permits the local production of new consumer services. Again, the economy has embarked on a pattern of import substitution which further enhances local prosperity by reducing leakages. More jobs are created within the urban economy, there is a greater degree of local self-sufficiency, and less funds escape to a rival urban economy.

The small town which began by capturing a single export firm has now matured into a fairly sizeable city. Its basic sector has expanded and concomitantly, its nonbasic sector has also achieved greater diversity and complexity. All these developments increase the city's attractiveness for new industries. If the nonbasic sector is sufficiently attractive, then the local economy will possess the attributes required to nurture new ventures. New export activities will locate in the city and a further round of growth will occur. More threshold levels will be surpassed, an even greater array of esoteric services will emerge, and eventually, the city will have moved up the urban hierarchy until it attains the status of a metropolitan area.

According to Thompson, this urban growth scenario can be conceptualized as a five-stage developmental process.

We might identify first the *Stage of Export Specialization* in which the local economy is the lengthened shadow of a single dominant industry or even a single firm. This initial stage gives way with growth and size to the *Stage of the Export Complex* in which local production broadens to other products and/or deepens by extending forward or backward in the stages of production, by adding local suppliers and/or consumers of intermediate products. Next, the *Stage of Economic Maturation* (local service sector puberty) follows in which the principal expansion of local activity is in the direction of replacing imports with new "own use" production; the local economy fills out in range and quality of both business and consumer services. Fourth, the *Stage of Regional Metropolis* is reached, when the local economy becomes a node connecting and controlling neighboring cities, once rivals and now satellites, and the export of services becomes a major economic function. One more common phase is the *Stage of Technical-Professional Virtuosity*; national eminence in some specialized skill or economic function is achieved.[7]

However, up to this point, Thompson has answered only one major question. He has yet to explain why cities decline. According to Thompson, growth stops because the momentum of the previous stage lacks sufficient strength to propel the city into the pattern prescribed for the succeeding higher stage.

Thus, the growth of a local economy may hesitate and stagnate between any of these stages if the momentum at the end of a phase is not strong enough to carry the economy to the point at which the mechanism of the next stage is activated. An insufficiency of momentum may be relative rather than absolute, especially with reference to the fourth stage, metropolitan formation. Typically, one city will rise from a group of rivals to become the mother city of the group. Whichever city gets the jump on the others and achieves early economic dominance usually finds that success breeds success as external economies of service industry agglomeration pave the way for progressive cumulative coups.[8]

In other words, a failure of momentum may be directly related to the disadvantage of a late start.

According to this logic, large cities that have captured the initial advantage should be relatively immune to adversity because an "urban size ratchet" inhibits absolute contraction.

> Perhaps some critical size exists, short of which growth is not inevitable and even the very existence of the place is not assured, but beyond which absolute contraction is highly unlikely, even though the growth rate may slacken, at times even to zero. In sum, at a certain range of urban scale ... some growth mechanisms similar to a ratchet, comes into being, locking in past growth and preventing contraction.[9]

Three forces activate the ratchet. First, a large city is more likely to develop a steady stream of inventions that continously inject new vigor into its industrial base.[10] Therefore, new export activities will always be available to replace dying or slowly growing export industries. Second, a diversified industrial structure coupled with a well-developed nonbasic sector ensures that contraction and decay will be highly improbable. Within the basic sector, diversification smooths both secular and cyclical swings. While one industry performs at an above average rate, others may lag. The net effect is relative stability and a local economy that neither grows very rapidly nor contracts for prolonged periods. A diversified, well-rounded nonbasic sector reinforces this tendency. Although some industries may be obsolete, an adequate nonbasic sector attracts replacements. Thus, "a diversified set of current exports—breadth—softens the shock of exogenous change, while a rich infrastructure—depth—facilitates the adjustment to change by providing the socio-economic institutions and physical facilities needed to initiate new enterprises, transfer capital from old to new forms, and retain labor."[11]

Finally, the phenomenon of filtering down or industrial spin-off may also activate the ratchet. Both Thompson and Jacobs hypothesize that as cities grow, certain industries are no longer viable in their present location. Due to high labor or land costs, for instance, they disappear from the local economy and are replaced by newer, locally invented, high-level industries that can bear the high costs associated with a metropolitan location. Thus, the loss of old industries does not signify economic decay. Rather, it is a symptom of economic health and vitality.

Since the addition of new industries crowds out the old, and since this mechanism is triggered by the addition of a more viable substitute, spinoff produces a high-quality industrial base. Thus, the comparative advantage of the large city vis-à-vis its smaller rivals increases and the prospect of economic decline recedes.

Smaller cities, by contrast, receive the industries spun off by their larger counterparts. These industries have been captured by small cities because they are dying, or are at a later stage of their product life cycle. As a result, "the smaller, less industrially advanced area struggles to achieve an average rate of growth out of enlarging shares of slow growth industries, originating as a by-product of the area's low wage rate attraction."[12]

Needless to say, this is a rather weak foundation on which to build a large and prosperous city. The low wages reduce the multiplier and depress the consumer service sector. This restricts consumer services to the simplest type while the lack of sufficient demand stifles the addition of new and more complex consumer services. In addition, since these export industries are near death and no longer need sophisticated business services, this sector also will decline. In short, capturing these industries almost guarantees that the growth momentum will not carry the small city into the next evolutionary stage. Moreover, as the industry decays and presumably reduces its payroll, the local economy will collapse and secular decline will appear. Thus, due to their insufficient momentum and inadequate industrial base, the ratchet effect does not apply to small cities.

However, these unfortunate locales may delay the day of reckoning through a vigorous program of industrial development that continually regenerates the sagging economy and captures newly spun-off activities. Big cities, on the other hand, can be relatively complacent about boosterism since only small cities that have been unable to activate the ratchet must worry about growth. Therefore, Thompson concludes his analysis of the ratchet by declaring, "Small wonder that the largest metropolitan areas can be so little concerned with promoting area industrial development, compared with the frantic activities of this kind conducted by the smaller areas."[13]

Some Recent Complications

In a recent article, Thompson has revised his optimistic analysis.[14] He now argues that due to a structural malfunction in both the spinoff and urbanization processes, the ratchet no longer applies to large cities. Two factors account for this change. First, Thompson argues that U.S. urbanization was never a rational process. Cities were not developed to meet specific needs but rather, the chaotic process of free competition created an oversupply of large urban areas that no longer possess any economic raison d'être. As a result, some of these cities will have to shrink and possibly cease functioning. With respect to this aspect, Thompson writes:

> We did not, for the most part, build great cities in this country; manufacturing firms agglomerated in tight industrial complexes and formed labor pools of half a million workers. That is not the same thing as building great cities. We sort of woke up one day and there was Cleveland.... Our great industrial transformation has left us with a large number of overgrown cities.[15]

The second malfunction relates to the spinoff process that was supposed to ensure the continued survival of large cities. Unfortunately, according to Thompson, large cities now spin off activities faster than they can generate replacements. In the past, the decline of manufacturing was seen as a device to create room for the service industries. This, in turn, would allow the large cities to participate in the postindustrial age. Today, this process has backfired. "Ten years ago, we all talked optimistically about the new age of services. What happened to this new force that was supposed to come in and rebuild the cores of our aging metropolises? . . . The service age just has not come to the fore with the passing of manufacturing to rescue the big cities the way it was supposed to—not yet anyway."[16] As a result, these cities must now cope with a perverse irony. If they are indeed moving toward a postindustrial age, it is due to their loss of industry and not the development of a healthy service sector.

Several comments concerning the stages of growth model are in order before we turn to the next group of urban growth theorists. First, recent employment trends in Northeastern cities should eliminate once and for all the concept of an urban size ratchet from the working vocabulary of urban analysts. With respect to both population and jobs, many urban areas in the Northeast have experienced prolonged periods of decline. This trend exists both for relatively small cities such as Providence and for some of the largest cities such as New York, Chicago, Detroit, and Philadelphia. Urban decay in other words is not a plague visited only on small cities. Rather, it shows no respect for size, and large cities are just as susceptible as their smaller and supposedly weaker counterparts.

Second, Thompson's statement that only small cities will be concerned with economic development is historically inaccurate. Although it is true that many older cities have been relatively unsuccessful in this endeavor, their failure cannot be attributed to a lack of effort or the application of insufficient funds.[17] Enormous resources have been dedicated to economic revitalization, and if these efforts have been failures, the cause must be attributed to other forces such as the relationship of these cities to the process of national economic development. When coupled with an analysis of the patterns of economic evolution, this investigation might explain why these cities have been unable to cope with change.

Finally, the stages of economic growth model fails to answer many pertinent questions. What factors have accelerated the spinoff from the older industrial cities? Why have newer cities been immune from this malady? If an urban size ratchet were a relevant description of past urban development patterns, what forces caused it to malfunction? Simply arguing that cities stop growing when the spinoff process accelerates is a tautological response that is tantamount to declaring that cities stop growing when their rate of growth slows down. It is true, but devoid of any information. Thus, while Thompson and Jacobs attempt to explore the dynamics of city growth, they never explain how cities develop and grow within the context of an evolving national economy.

THE EPOCHS OF URBAN GROWTH MODEL

A second group of urban growth theorists claim that the stages of growth model presents an oversimplified version of urban dynamics. In response to this flaw, their models assume that historical eras vary with respect to both their internal dynamics and the activities that promote urban growth. Thus, as the economy moves through successive epochs, the composition of dynamic industries change. Unless the urban economy can change in unison with the national economy, it will become saddled with an outmoded industrial structure.

In this section, we will discuss some of the major concepts that comprise these alternative growth theories. The analysis will be divided into four subsections: (1) the relationship between the division of labor and urbanization, (2) the theory of cumulative causation and mutual feedback, (3) the dynamics of the mercantile era, and (4) the dynamics of the industrial era.

The Division of Labor and the Process of Urbanization

The first question that must be answered is why do we have cities? According to Lampard, cities are not simply passive agents in the development process. Although they happened to be the place where displaced agricultural workers congregated and where factories were established, they were more than repositories for an uprooted, unemployed agricultural population. Cities also stimulated the cultural and economic transformation required by the capitalist system. The industrial revolution "was a phase of cultural history in which certain communities became marked by an increasing differentiation of economic functions, skills, instruments, institutions, and regions. It was this ongoing specialization . . . which gradually transformed the techno-organizational base of society and, with it, the spatial order of economic activities."[18]

Yet, according to Lampard, "location theorists and land economists . . . rarely went on to link their discussion of the spatial factors to the more complex phenomenon of economic growth. . . . No branch of economics yet studies the city in a comprehensive way. . . . No systematic study has even been made of the role of cities in recent economic development."[19] Therefore, in order to fashion this link between urbanization and development, Lampard investigates the process of specialization, which he claims is the basis for the existence of cities.

Broken down to its simplest element, location theory is nothing more than a description of the economic forces creating spatial specialization. Certain regions or cities specialize in one activity because they are the best site for a particular industry. Through the process of spatial specialization, scarce resources are conserved (transport inputs, for example) and profits are maximized. However, spatial specialization rests upon one essential ingredient. Before there can be a spatial division of labor there must be a social division of labor that transforms each individual into a specialist with one task to perform. The rationale for the social division of labor is identical to the rationale supporting an efficient spatial distribution of economic activity: "The object of specialization, therefore, is a greater economy of time, effort and resources—the sources of higher productivity and advance."[20]

Were specialization an isolated phenomenon instituted for special occasions, there would be little need for cities and the ensuing spatial division of labor. Every area would be self-sufficient, and the occasional episodes of specialization would hardly affect settlement patterns. Therefore, for specialization to have any lasting effects, there must be a proper "sociopsychological atmosphere" that makes specialization "no longer a matter of taste or inclination, but a condition of survival and fulfillment." When these conditions exist, specialization assumes a life of its own. The initial act of specialization "will thrive best where it is most developed. Specialization tends to breed specialization."[21]

But specialization breeds more than simply additional specialization. The quantitative increase in the degree of specialization soon requires a qualitative change in the coordinating apparatus of society. This qualitative imperative contains both an institutional and an ecological[22] dimension and results from the need to "impose a greater measure of interdependence among the differentiated parts."

> Sometimes the interdependence is *indirect* (social) in the sense that everyone in the community now sinks or swims together. . . . *Direct* interdependence, on the other hand, is ecological: it arises from the necessity of overcoming structural and environmental *frictions* which may impede the smooth, efficient operation of differentiated parts.[23]

Thus, the need for both direct and indirect integration sets centripetal forces in motion. Activities that were formerly both universal and ubiquitous now relocate in cities where they can be conducted in a rational and efficient manner. As a result, "the growth of the modern city and the march of the industrial revolution are joint products of a single cultural strand—specialization. . . . From the socio-ecological standpoint, city growth is simply the concentration of differentiated but functionally integrated specialisms in rational locales. The modern city is a mode of social organization which furthers efficiency in economic activity."[24]

Cumulative Causation and Positive Feedback

To argue that cities are a precondition for specialization and economic change conveys little information about the process of urban development. But before this process can be understood in a concrete historical form, Lampard believes that it is necessary to discuss certain abstract concepts contained in systems theory. Only after he has examined the forces of growth and development within a system does Lampard feel that he will be able to understand the stresses and strains placed upon a single city, which, after all, is only one element of a much larger system.

The first distinction that requires elucidation is the one between growth and development. Growth signifies the increasing magnitude of a system whose basic structures remain unchanged. Development, a more dialectical concept, assumes that quantitative changes produce qualitative alterations in the system's basic structure. As one component of the system grows in magnitude, it alters its relationship to both the other elements and the totality. But this is not a random or chaotic process. For the system to remain viable, it must

> shape the parts so that each part functions to preserve the existence and general structure of the whole. . . . Consequently, we can interpret the relationships within the totality according to the way in which they function to preserve and reproduce it. . . . But these relationships are not necessarily in harmony with each other. They are frequently in contradiction and out of this contradiction flows conflict. Transformations occur through the resolution of these conflicts and with each transformation, the totality is restructured and this restructuring in turn, alters the definition, meaning, and function of the elements and relationships within the whole. New conflicts and contradictions emerge to replace the old.[25]

According to Lampard, general equilibrium theory is not conducive to understanding either the relationships between a set of fluid concepts or the dynamics of this fluidity. During the process of development, we "learn or evolve new structures and behaviour so as to remain stable under changing conditions. We adapt to a changing environment through a process of learning and innovation."[26] Unfortunately, equilibrium theory assumes that the basic structures are unchanged.[27] Since in the long run, all quantitative changes produce irreversible qualitative changes, the concept of equilibrium becomes meaningless. With no stable frame of reference the system can never return to homeostasis and must be constantly in disequilibrium.

Furthermore, the concept of an evolving system is the antithesis of an equilibrated system. A system may be defined as a "complex of component objects possessing certain attributes as economic centers. The system is tied together by the relationships among its components whose attributes are thereby subjected to change and may, in turn, affect the system."[28] But the interaction of the various components can lead to either of two outcomes. Traditional equilibrium theory only considers negative feedback or morphostasis, which can be characterized as "deviation counteracting feedback networks."[29] In this state of affairs development is impossible since every change is immediately counteracted by forces that return the system to the previous status quo. Development requires positive feedback or morphogenesis, which involves "deviation amplifying and system transforming" changes. However, a chain reaction, whereby one change induces further changes that push the system farther from the original status quo (the process of development) is clearly not an equilibrating system.

Yet, at the same time, deviation-amplifying changes do not always entail an uncontrolled, explosive reaction. Certain stabilizing forces may exist which allow the entire system to advance in an orderly fashion. For example, under certain conditions, one part of the system may develop at the expense of another part (uneven development) or one part may advance and then pause while the other sectors catch up. The precise pattern depends upon the characteristics of the system and the particular relationships that exist during specific evolutionary stages. Therefore, it is impossible to propose abstract, general rules. Instead, we must study concrete historical examples and recognize that different patterns may emerge during different epochs.

Urban Development During the Mercantile and Industrial Eras

According to the economic historian N.S.B. Gras, "Mercantilism was the policy of the town writ large in the affairs of the state. . . . In the first phase of metropolitan economy the chief concern of the metropolitan unit was not so much advance in industry as reorganization of the marketing system."[30] Under mercantilism, each city is primarily concerned with carving out the most extensive hinterland possible in order to dominate the economic life of rival cities. The result is an economic landscape that can best be described as a "mosaic of resource regions" with each region dominated by a few major urban centers. In short, during this period, the economic relations between a city and its hinterland most closely resemble the typical patterns described in the central place literature.

Economic policy during this period is directly motivated by the goal of "preventing the tributary territory from trading with other towns. The cattle and dairy products must be sent to the town market in order to keep down the cost of living of the townspeople; it would not do to have *their* produce go to other towns."[31]

Of course, cities could expand their local hinterland by improving transportation. The city which could most effectively penetrate a resource region with cheap transportation arteries would be able to widen its supply area at the expense of rival commercial centers. Therefore, during the mercantile phase of urbanization, the construction of transportation facilities, warehouse facilities, and the supply of commercial services such as banking and freight forwarding provided the greatest boost to the local economy.

Until approximately 1840, wholesaling and retailing dominated the urban economy.[32] Manufacturing, on the other hand, could not gain a foothold and boost the city's rate of growth. Its weakness can be attributed to the higher profits associated with land speculation and commerce, a dependence on water power which inhibited geographic concentration and mass production, and a poor transportation network which limited the size of the accessible market and offset economies of scale.

Due to these preindustrial conditions, the dynamics of mercantile urban growth differed substantially from the dynamic forces that existed after the industrial revolution. To illustrate these differences, assume that a mercantile city increases its commerce by building a canal linking the city to the interior. This initial boost causes mercantile-related manufacturing activities to expand and produces even faster growth. However, in these preindustrial conditions, this process cannot sustain itself without constant exogenous shocks from the commercial sector. Manufacturing is simply unable to generate the momentum required for self-sustained growth. As a result, the stimulus provided by this sector soon dissipates and the system returns to equilibrium. In other words, during the mercantile phase of urban growth, the morphogenetic forces cannot alter the system's basic structures.

However, sometime between 1840 and 1860, significant changes occurred within both the national and local economies that endowed manufacturing with morphogenetic effects. Consequently, the forces of specialization modified the economic landscape and manufacturing, which previously had been of secondary importance, became the most prominent features of the urban economy.

Several factors account for the centripetal tendencies set in motion by the industrial revolution. With better transportation, the raw material site exerted less influence on the location of manufacturing. While some activities remained tied to the raw material site even with the lower freight rates, many others developed a market orientation. Once proximity to markets dominated the location calculus, "then it might be expected that the great commercial centers should also be the manufacturing centers, for they not only contain a rich and numerous body of consumers, but apparently afford superior facilities for distributing goods to the remaining consuming population." Thus, cheap transportation and a large market allowed the large commercial city to compete effectively with a small town situated adjacent to the raw materials.

Large-scale factories promoted an advance stage of specialization and urbanization. For a variety of reasons—economy in motive power, economy in machinery, savings in unit wage costs brought about by a more extensive division of labor, economy in the use of byproducts, and special facilities for buying selling, shipping, and warehousing—modern enterprise was more cost effective when operated on a large scale. This fact both required and generated large cities. Either the plant would locate in a large, already established city in order to profit from the large labor pool or else the plant would choose a smaller center for its production site, and its presence would create a large city. In either case, the correlation between factory production and large cities was unmistakable.

Given this association, how was the dynamic process of urban growth affected by the industrial revolution? According to Pred, an industrial revolution model of urban growth must include three concepts: the urban multiplier, initial advantage, and threshold. The threshold concept suggests that each activity has a "minimum population or volume of sales required to support a new optimum scale factory or addition to existing facilities."[34] It is a function of the prevailing level of technology and increases in tandem with technological breakthroughs. Because of this trend, the possibility that a small city can break into the upper levels of the urban hierarchy decreases. Thus, those cities that have already achieved a certain minimum size by dint of development in an earlier era, have the initial advantage required to maintain their growth.

> As thresholds reached higher and higher levels, and as the optimal scale of operation for raw material and footloose (nonthreshold) factories grew, the possibility of entry into the market or expansion of existing facilities became confined to a smaller and smaller number of cities, and many manufacturing functions shifted from lower order to higher order urban places and/or became more geographically concentrated.[35]

As a result, those regions that have already surpassed the minimum threshold required for the exploitation of these scale economies will be in a better position to attract new activities.

Any exogenous shock delivered to their industrial base will have a large multiplier effect which, in turn, propels the city into further rounds of growth.

Because of these attributes, change will be self-reinforcing and for the large cities, negative feedback will not counteract this process.

Summary and Critical Comments

This model offers many improvements over the scenario proposed by Thompson and Jacobs. Perhaps its greatest contribution is its recognition that urban growth is not an historically homogeneous process. By concentrating on the dynamic processes at work during different stages of economic development, Pred and Lampard have developed a model that includes history as an important developmental variable.

Yet despite this advantage, the model leaves many questions unanswered. For instance, Thompson argues that industrial spinoff is an important phase of urban growth since it allows large cities to eliminate low-level activities. Pred, on the other hand, proposes an opposite scenario. In his model, small cities spin off their activities to large cities so that they can be reorganized according to the dictates of large-scale efficiency. Thus, while both models accept the existence of spinoff, the implications and directions of this process remain unclear.

Furthermore, the Pred-Lampard model never discusses urban decay. Basically, they agree with Thompson and argue that big cities possess an initial advantage that precludes slow growth or decline. When slow growth does enter the Lampard-Pred model, it is due to a lack of momentum which prevents the forces of morphogenesis from dominating the forces of morphostasis. But again, this is a tautological argument. They fail to explain why this occurs.

Finally, the Lampard-Pred model does not explain how the transition from a mercantile base to an industrial base affects the urban economy. What happens to a city that developed during the mercantile era? It is true, as Pred illustrates, that some cities such as Pittsburgh, Chicago, and Cleveland were able to transform their economic base and conform to the needs of the new phase. But is this true for all cities? If not, does a city's failure to transform its economy imply that it will die or only that its stage of rapid growth has come to an end? Also, if the rise of the Sunbelt signals the emergence of a third era of urbanization, then we must ask how this affects those cities that survived and prospered during the previous two stages. Not only does the model fail to deal with this third wave, but its inability to describe the effect of evolutionary transitions on older areas limits its utility as a tool for analyzing the current forces creating uneven development.

NOTES

1. Some of the more notable city classification systems can be found in Brian Berry (ed.), *City Classifications Handbook* (New York: John Wiley, 1972); Harvey Perloff et al., *Regions, Resources and Economic Growth* (Baltimore: Johns Hopkins Univ. Press, 1960); Howard Nelson, "A Service Classification of U.S. Cities," *Economic Geography* 31, 2 (1955): 189-210; Chauncy Harris, "A Functional Classification of Cities in the United States," *Geographical Review* 33, 1 (1943): 86-99; and Gunnar Alexandersson, *The Industrial Structure of American Cities* (Lincoln: Univ. of Nebraska Press, 1956).

2. Otis Dudley Duncan et al., *Metropolis and Region* (Baltimore: Johns Hopkins Univ. Press, 1960): 204.

3. Eric E. Lampard, 'The Evolving System of Cities in the United States: Urbanization and Economic Development," in Harvey Perloff and Lowdon Wingo (eds.), *Issues in Urban Economics* (Baltimore: Johns Hopkins Univ. Press, 1968): 93-94.

4. Wilbur Thompson, *A Preface to Urban Economics* (Baltimore: Johns Hopkins Univ. Press, 1968) and "Internal and External Factors in the Development of Urban Economies," in Harvey Perloff and Lowdon Wingo (eds.), op. cit.: 43-62.

5. Jane Jacobs, *The Economy of Cities* (New York: Random House, 1969).

6. Thompson, "Internal and External Factors": 46.

7. Thompson, *A Preface to Urban Economics:* 15-16.

8. Ibid.: 17.

9. Ibid.: 22.

10. For some empirical studies detailing the higher incidence of innovation in large cities see Robert Higgs, "American Inventiveness, 1870-1920," *Journal of*

Political Economy 79, 3 (1971): 661-667; Irwin Feller, "The Urban Location of U.S. Invention, 1860-1910," *Explorations in Entrepreneurial History* 8, 3 (1971): 285-304; Allan Pred, "Large City Interdependence and the Pre-Electronic Diffusion of Innovations in the U.S.," *Geographical Analysis* 3, 2 (1971): 165-181.

11. Thompson, "Internal and External Factors": 53.

12. Ibid.: 56.

13. Ibid.: 54.

14. Wilbur Thompson, "Economic Process and Employment Problems in Declining Metropolitan Areas," in George Sternlieb and James W. Hughes, *Post Industrial America: Metropolitan Decline and Inter-Regional Job Shifts* (New Brunswick, NJ: Center for Urban Policy Research, 1975).

15. Ibid.: 189.

16. Ibid.: 191-192.

17. Case studies of various efforts to upgrade the central city and make it a more viable location are discussed in John Mollenkopf, "The Post-War Politics of Urban Development," *Politics and Society* 5, 3 (1975): 247-296; Robert Caro, *The Power Broker* (New York: Random House, 1975); and Roy Lubove, *Twentieth Century Pittsburgh* (New York: John Wiley, 1969).

18. Eric E. Lampard, "The History of Cities in the Economically Advanced Areas," *Economic Development and Cultural Change* 3, 2 (1955): 81-136.

19. Ibid.: 83-84.

20. Ibid.: 89.

21. Ibid.: 89.

22. The sociological concept of ecology was developed by a group of urban sociologists at the University of Chicago. Their analysis focused on the relationship between various neighborhoods and was dubbed "human ecology." In addition, another group of scholars used ecological terminology to characterize the pattern of intercity relationships. For a discussion of the human ecology literature, see Richard Sennett, *Classic Essays on the Culture of Cities* (New York: Appleton-Century-Crofts, 1969): 91-179; and Amos Hawley, *Human Ecology* (New York: Ronald Press, 1950). For a discussion of urban ecology, see Roderick D. McKenzie, *The Metropolitan Community* (New York: McGraw-Hill, 1933); N.S.B. Gras, *An Introduction to Economic History* (New York: Harper & Brothers, 1922); and Donald J. Bogue, *The Structure of the Metropolitan Community: A Study of Dominance and Sub-Dominance* (Ann Arbor: Univ. of Michigan Press, 1949).

23. Lampard, "The History of Cities . . .": 90-91.

24. Ibid.: 91-92.

25. David Harvey, *Social Justice and the City* (Baltimore: Johns Hopkins Univ. Press, 1973): 289.

26. Mervyn L. Cadwallader, "The Cybernetic Analysis of Change in Complex Social Organizations," *American Journal of Sociology* 65, 2 (1959): 155.

27. For a more detailed analysis of the problems inherent in equilibrium analysis, see Adolph Lowe, *On Economic Knowledge* (New York: Harper & Row, 1965): Chapter 11.

28. Lampard, "The History of Cities . . .": 97.

29. This terminology is adopted from Magoroh Maruyama, "The Second Cybernetics: Deviation Amplifying Mutual Causal Processes," *General Systems* 8, 2 (1963): 233-241.

30. Gras, op. cit.: 201, 203.

31. Adna Ferrin Weber, *The Growth of Cities in the Nineteenth Century* (Ithaca, NY: Cornell Univ. Press, 1963): 177.

32. This section is a brief summary of the model presented by Allan Pred, *The Spatial Dynamics of U.S. Urban Industrial Growth, 1800-1914* (Cambridge, MA: MIT Press, 1966): 143-190.

33. Weber, op. cit.: 198.

34. Pred, *Spatial Dynamics:* 33.

35. Ibid.: 60-61.

Chapter 6

AN ALTERNATIVE MODEL OF URBAN DYNAMICS

A model of urban dynamics cannot be developed in an historical vacuum. Instead, a realistic model must recognize that cities grow, mature, and decay within the context of historical forces that are intimately related to the evolutionary trends propelling the national economy from one developmental stage to the next. Therefore, the model must reflect, in some sense, a notion of the correspondence between changes in the national economy and their impact on the local economy.

Most of the dynamic models of urban development discussed in the previous chapter do posit a strong correlation between the stage of development attained by the national economy and the matrix of rapidly growing industries that transform a city from an insignificant urban center to the core city of a metropolitan area. However, these traditional models fail to distinguish between the theoretical requirements for continued rapid growth and the actual experience of specific cities as they try to prosper within the context of a national economy moving from one developmental stage to the next. According to these models, either the process of import substitution, export development and industrial spinoff, or the process of cumulative causation and initial advantage create continuous flux and turmoil as local entrepreneurs attempt to adjust to the new stage of national economic development. Although they disagree on the precise mechanisms creating these periodic episodes of industrial upheaval, all of the theories contend that dramatic shifts within the national economy produced similar changes within each city's industrial structure. The typical healthy city, they claim, will successfully navigate this transition; those aberrant cities that fail in this endeavor are doomed to eventual obsolescence or at best, perpetual slow growth.

Historical evidence, however, suggests that the typical city is not blessed with a periodic revitalization of its economic base. Although it is probably correct to assume that most businessmen want to maintain their cities in the vanguard of industrial progress, their rate of success is quite dismal, and these failures have been amply documented. On the international level, for example, both Veblen and Rostow argue quite forcefully that the British industrial base, which earlier had been adequate to propel Britain to the top rank among industrial nations, soon ossified as the forces of complacency and inertia inhibited the rejuvenation that Britain needed to retain her dominant economic position.[1] As a result, Germany, unencumbered by outmoded practices and infrastructure, latched on to the new, technologically sophisticated activities spawned during a later industrial epoch and eventually replaced Britain at the pinnacle of the industrial world.

Closer to home, other observers have been careful to distinguish between the theoretical requirements for continued rapid urban growth and the empirical reality plaguing many U.S. cities. Generally, they conclude that a city has only one relatively brief period of rapid growth which is directly related to the vibrancy of the industries that comprise its economic base. Once its industrial structure has matured, however, the entire dynamic process of city growth grinds to a halt despite the most vigorous efforts to revitalize the local economy. For example, in a discussion of the problems afflicting Pittsburgh, Hoover laments:

> Pittsburgh faces a challenge of transition which to date it has not fully succeeded in meeting. . . . This occurred partly because so much of Pittsburgh's earlier pre-eminence was based on specialization in industries which themselves are no longer expanding in terms of employment . . . and have all been downgraded in importance by technological and market shifts. . . . Rapid technological change means rapid obsolescence of physical facilities and skills alike. By that token, it poses particularly serious adjustment problems to areas like the Pittsburgh region which have especially large proportions of their physical and human resources committed in terms of earlier technical conditions. . . . The adaptability of workers and business firms to new tasks and opportunities is less when a high proportion of those workers and firms have been doing substantially the same thing for a long time and have acquired a large stake in the status quo.[2]

More recently, the New York *Times* provided an update of economic conditions in Pittsburgh. Although thirteen years had elapsed since Hoover's remarks, their diagnoses were remarkably similar; despite massive efforts and even some success in revitalizing the central business district, Pittsburgh has been unable to replace the steel industry with new activities and thus recapture the rapid growth rates of the late nineteenth century.

> The entire Crescent has entered an age of cutting back as manufacturing has declined in the total economy and as the competing Sunbelt attracts money, industry, and talent. Many of the Crescent's metropolitan areas, not merely the aging central cities, are losing population. Metropolitan Pittsburgh is leading the way. It has been losing population since the 1960s. . . . Downtown renaissance notwithstanding, Pittsburgh proper had an estimated population drop of 8.4 percent between 1970 and 1975. . . . Some steel mills have closed here in the last two decades and automation has caused the workforce to further decline. When new mills are built, they are usually built elsewhere.[3]

In conjunction with these empirical observations, several other scholars suggest a different scenario to explain the impact that changes in the national economy produce on the local industrial structure.[4] In their opinion, cities generally do not undergo periodic renewals of their industrial base. Instead, new industries, riding the crest of a new technological breakthrough, tend to locate in new cities. Because of the rapid employment growth generated by these new industries, the newer cities also experience rapid population growth while the old cities, saddled with a slowly growing or shrinking industrial base, expand at a relatively slow pace.

CAPITAL ACCUMULATION AND URBAN DYNAMICS

With these empirical and theoretical observations as a foundation we can begin to develop the outline of a more complete theory of urban growth and decay. This theory contains three major components:

(1) As an economy develops and passes through succeeding evolutionary stages, different methods of capital accumulation and economic activities emerge as the dominant, leading edge sectors. In other words, within each epoch a few rapidly growing industries promote the growth and prosperity of the entire economy. As that particular epoch wanes and the economy passes to a new developmental era, a new array of industries emerge to carry the national economy to new heights of prosperity. However, during this transformation, the old, formerly dominant activities do not disappear. They simply recede into the background, no longer serving as the *foundation* for the new developmental wave.

(2) Each stage of capital accumulation is linked directly to fairly distinct waves of urban development. More precisely, because those new industries spawned by the new phase of capital accumulation tend to locate in new cities, each succeeding developmental epoch generates rapid population and employment growth in a different set of cities. In the meantime, those older cities whose formative era was associated with a previous developmental stage are not significantly affected by

the economic transformation. They simply continue to perform their old functions despite the fact that these activities are no longer capable of sustaining rapid urban growth. None of these implications bodes well for the mature city, but as long as its industrial base continues to generate income and avoid obsolescence, it will carry out its old functions and continue to fill its old role just as if nothing has happened.

In short, the model assumes that the system of cities evolves and adds new members by a very selective process. New cities develop by capturing a large share of those activities that are at an early stage in the product life cycle while old cities, which are growing very slowly or even stagnating, have been unable to rejuvenate themselves because their industrial structure contains only those activities that are at a much later stage in the product life cycle. As these old activities stagnate, the city's growth will decline to negligible levels; when the industries actually become obsolete and start to decline absolutely, the city will start to lose jobs and population.

Several qualifications are necessary before we move to the next component of this theoretical model. First, the statement that new activities tend to locate in new cities does not exclude the possibility that an old city will generate some growth on the basis of these new activities. Instead, the theory posits that these developments will be marginal and thus will not alter the basic characteristics of its industrial structure. New activities will only produce a minimal generative impact in old cities while in the new cities the basic "personality" of its industrial structure will reflect the presence of these new industries.

Second, this analysis does not deny the existence of a spinoff mechanism. Spinoff does occur, but this process implies something quite different from the explanation provided by Thompson and Jacobs. If a city spins off an activity which is essential to its economic base, then this signals the impending death of the city. New England textile and shoe towns and Youngstown, Ohio are only a few vivid illustrations of the fate awaiting an urban area when it loses part of its economic base. Since their ability to generate replacements is rather limited, they become sick, and possibly even dying, cities.

Third, the notion that mature cities "are not significantly affected" requires further elaboration. Obviously, in a relative sense, and possibly in an absolute sense, old cities are affected by the location of new industries in new cities. The actual growth rate and level of prosperity would be much greater if these new activities would locate in the old cities. Certainly, businessmen and other residents of older cities cannot treat this location decision with equanimity. It implies that jobs and potential profits have been diverted to other regions; that new competing centers can heighten the competition for any new activities that may emerge later; that the momentum of an early start has been dissipated and possibly was of little long-run advantage; and most importantly, that the mature city is saddled with relatively stagnant industries while the new city, acting without the benefit of an initial advantage, has captured the new growth-inducing activities. None of these facts bodes well for the mature city, and thus the failure to attract the new dynamic activity most definitely affects the city. Yet in another sense the city has remained unaffected. Its industrial structure, while certainly not helped by the creation of new cities, has not been harmed either. If the city retains its old industries and if these continue to generate income, the city can avoid collapse. Thus, unless the city's industrial structure becomes obsolete, it has indeed been relatively little affected by these events. The city will continue with its old functions and fill its old role just as if nothing has happened.

Fourth, the argument that a city's industrial base generally resists periodic transformations should not be interpreted to imply that once a city's economy matures, all outside pressures and technological changes are of no import. Clearly, the industries found in old cities have altered their technological sophistication in accordance with the general developments in society. The garment industry in New York, for example, does not operate without electricity, and the banking and commercial sector has been affected by the introduction of computers and other data-processing devices. But while the computer industry has developed into a new and modern leading edge sector, it has not altered the economic base of New York. Banking and finance were present before the introduction of computers, and they continue to dominate New York's economic base today. The tools used by the banking and finance industry have been upgraded because of this innovation, but the banking industry's importance to New York's economy has not changed.

Finally, the claim that a city will be unable to renew its industrial structure by adding new activities should not be viewed as some immutable and natural law. It is only a statement concerning a tendency that appears to characterize the historical experience of American cities. Certainly, there is nothing internal to a mature city's industrial structure which precludes this regenerative possibility. However, since the incidence of economic regeneration has been exceedingly rare, a general theory of urban dynamics should not be predicated on the assumption that a city will continually renew its economic base. Yet at the same time, the recent literature discussing the prospects for an "urban renaissance" stimulated by the phenomenon of "gentrification" would seem to indicate that, at least for a select group of cities, a tentative process of urban rejuvenation may be beginning.[5] According to this scenario, some of the moribund central cities in the Northeast will gain a new lease on life as a wealthy, well-educated, professional elite reclaims many downtown neighborhoods from their former, mostly poor occupants. Although this would entail continued population declines, the new demographic mix and new economic activities spawned by this process would provide the city with a more stable and sustainable economic base. Should this occur, it would represent one of the few successful episodes in which a group of cities substantially altered the character and quality of its industrial foundation.

(3) In view of the preceding assertion that old cities do not partake in the new wave of capital accumulation because it is difficult for them to renew their economic base, the final component of this theory must account for the problems old cities face when they try to capture a new generation of leading edge industries and the relative ease with which new cities

accomplish this same task. We can provide this missing link by grafting the concept of developmental barriers to the preceding two components.

The concept of barriers, as employed in this paper, denotes a rather complex matrix of pressures and internally generated contradictions that limit the development of a group of cities tied to a particular, unchanging set of industries. The alternating influence of these barriers creates the shifting rhythms and patterns of uneven urban development that characterize the historical evolution of the U.S. system of cities. Specifically, barriers operate in two directions; at one time they may be viewed as analogous to protective tariffs, while at a later date, they serve as fetters blocking the city's adoption of a new set of dynamic activities.

During the period before a specific phase of capital accumulation has spent its generative potential, the dominant cities erect various institutional and structural barriers which thwart the entry of other subordinate cities into the upper echelons of the urban hierarchy. By limiting the number of competing urban centers, the dominant cities inhibit the growth of their less developed counterparts and thus make it more difficult for them to capture a significant portion of the leading edge activities. This latter group of cities is relegated to the role of satellite or perhaps a favored colony. They are the hinterland outposts in an urban system whose development is controlled and regulated by the decisions of the dominant cities. As such, their failure to grow and develop emanates from the growth and prosperity of their dominant rivals.

However, each epoch, if it has successfully fulfilled its developmental function, soon generates a set of contradictions which preclude further capital accumulation based upon the old and now obsolete practices.[6] As a result, those cities which had previously created a set of barriers to insure their dominance in a particular sphere of economic activity become trapped by their own actions. Unless they can overcome their addiction to these old activities and transform their economies so that they are once again in harmony with the requirements generated by the succeeding wave of capital accumulation, their local economy will ossify and their position as growth leader will wane. The benefits flowing from their initial advantage during one developmental stage are transformed into barriers that inhibit the emergence of a new, generative industrial base.

At this point, these barriers represent an opportunity for those cities that formerly had been relegated to a subordinate role. As one epoch wanes, a new and different set of possibilities for further capital accumulation appears on the horizon. Unencumbered by the now outmoded practices which characterized the previous era and which immobilized the businessmen wedded to the old methods and practices, these entrepreneurs build a new set of dynamic cities based upon a modern approach to capital accumulation. In the process, however, they, too, erect a set of protective barriers only to be consumed by them at a later date.

In summation, within each epoch, the barriers erected by the dominant cities produce uneven development. The dominant cities prosper by inhibiting the development of their potential rivals. However, the role of dominant and subordinate urban areas is not immutably fixed. Once the dominant cities encounter a set of internally generated barriers, their growth slows and opportunities arise for some of the subordinate cities to emerge from their colonial status and initiate a new wave of divergent development.

A NOTE ON INDUSTRIAL LIFE CYCLES

The preceding theory assumes that industries follow a relatively stylized growth pattern that influences the city's growth profile. Specifically, the model suggests that during its early stages, an industry grows at a rapid rate while during its era of maturity, the growth rate slackens considerably. What factors contribute to this process of "industrial retardation?"

In his classic study of production trends in the United States between 1870 and 1925, Burns argues that industrial retardation is a normal and even desirable feature of economic progress and development. He presents five arguments to support this assertion.[7]

(1) Retardation is characteristic of a progressive economy. Assume that an economy grows "at a uniform percentage rate over a period of sizable duration" and that it regularly spawns new industries. If the new industries have rapid growth rates, then the growth rate of older industries must decline in order to keep the total economy growing at a steady rate. Since the appearance of new industries is one aspect of development, the retardation of old industries must also be viewed as part of this same process.

(2) Various market forces promote retardation. Specifically, technological change leads to the production of commodities that serve as substitutes for old products. This, in turn, induces "an absolute or relative shift in purchasing power" away from the old industries which can no longer continue their pace of rapid growth.

(3) Several retarding forces also operate in the "workshops of the economy." Just as the development of new commodities diverts purchasing power from the old industries, the same process reduces the flow of capital and resources to old industries. With a greater difficulty in obtaining the needed supplies, retardation occurs in the old industries.

In addition, Burns argues that the rate of technical progress within an industry is the main determinant of its growth rate. Although old industries also experience technological change, these advances are generally minor and do not dramatically revolutionize the methods of production. "Ordinarily, however, technical progress contributes more to the competitive power of the new than of the old industries, for technical progress is ordinarily more rapid in the early than in the late stages of the development of industries. Technical progress tends to proceed at a declining rate because the possibilities of progress within any given industry are limited."[8]

(4) Retardation within the system of industries tends to be cumulative as the retarding forces spread from industry to industry. Once an industry experiences the first wave of retarda-

tion, it will take steps to offset this development and hopefully even reverse the trend, generally by increasing the sales and research effort. Other industries that have avoided retardation will also take similar steps, but their actions are stimulated by precautionary motivations. Irrespective of the reasons prompting these actions,

> the industries which succeed in maintaining or extending their markets, through the pursuit of technical research and large scale salesmanship, intensify by the very fact of their success the difficulties of other industries. As technical research and salesmanship are cultivated more intensively, the tempo of industrial change is increased. Every technical betterment or marketing gesture releases fresh forces making for retardation in the growth of individual industries. So, the forces making for retardation, earlier analyzed, are seen to cumulate in strength; once released they are not soon spent, but rather gain momentum.[9]

(5) Industrial retardation will, under certain circumstances, be transformed into a process of industrial decadence. Retardation implies that growth still occurs although the rate of growth is declining. However, if retardation is either sufficiently rapid or proceeds for a long enough period, the positive rate of growth will give way to absolute decline.

Decadent industries comprise two groups. The first encompasses those industries that have vanished completely. The second group contains industries whose absolute decline has been checked as a result of the increased "resistance offered by the declining industry to further inroads on its market. . . . The smaller the output of a declining industry, the greater is such resistance likely to be; for, with a small output, the industry comes to satisfy fairly tenacious and impregnable wants."[10]

In view of these pervasive forces that produce industrial retardation, Burns formulates the following law of industrial growth:

> In the course of the life history of an industry, forces making for advance always act in combination with forces making for deca-

dence, their balance determining whether a rise or decline takes place. Once the forces making for decline continue to gain in relative strength, they will at some point come to equal and then surpass the forces making for advance; so that the rise will culminate in an apex and be succeeded by a decline. It is difficult, therefore, to find any sound rational basis for the notion that industries grow until they approximate some maximum size and then maintain a sationary position for an indefinite period. Nor is the notion at all supported by experience: *the production records of our industries practically never evidence a plateau at the apex; once an industry has ceased to advance, it rarely remains at a stationary level for any length of time, but rather soon embarks on a career of decadence.*[11]

THE MEASUREMENT OF URBAN AGE

The preceding discussion offers a new theory of urban development that explicitly links urban growth to the dynamic qualities of the industries that comprise each city's industrial base. This section will discuss the concept of urban age in order to determine the stage of capital accumulation that has most directly influenced each particular city. Once we have assigned each city to a specific era, it should then be possible to test the hypothesis that cities which develop during the same era have similar industrial structures, while cities that emerge during different periods possess qualitatively different industrial foundations.

Procedures for Dating Cities

In an attempt to provide greater precision to the concepts "old" city and "new" city, geographers, sociologists, and economists have devised various measures of urban age. Yet, as we will see, these dating procedures have serious flaws. Essentially, they use historical concepts in a ahistorical manner. Instead of devising a procedure that corresponds to the actual growth and development patterns in urban areas, they utilize mechanistic, arbitrary algorithms.

Schnore, for example, dates cities by counting the number of decades that have elapsed since each city first attained a population of 50,000.[12] Old cities attained this figure on or before 1910. He assigns all the other cities to the "new" category. Although this procedure has the advantage of simplicity, its defects outweigh its merits. In the first place, this algorithm cannot be used to assign a date to small urban centers that have not yet attained metropolitan status. More importantly, by positing an historically invariant threshold, Schnore fails to relate his dating procedure to the qualitative and quantitative changes that accompany industrial progress and continuous urbanization. Yet considerable evidence suggests that technological change, besides increasing industrial productivity, also raises the critical threshold required to support a specific activity. Pred, for example, argues that "the spatial lengthening of production raised the threshold of some industries by increasing their minimum optimal scale of operation."[13] Other analysts question the accuracy of defining metropolitan status on the basis of a temporally constant threshold. They contend that if 50,000 is the critical size for present purposes, then a lower threshold should be utilized for earlier decades.[14] They claim, in essence, that an historically invariant threshold devalues the metropolitan concept by making it progressively "easier" for a city to attain this status. A city which grew to 50,000 population in 1810, before the introduction of modern technology, mass production, and national markets, would be among the one or two dominant metropolises in the nation; a city that attained this size in 1970 would be comparatively less significant. Schnore, unfortunately, never considers this possibility, and this omission seriously weakens the analytic utility of his dating procedure.

In an attempt to avoid the use of an absolute population threshold, Duncan and Lieberson date cities by counting the number of decades since the city's population first exceeded New Orleans's population.[15] Although this technique does provide a varying threshold which increases in tempo with the technological interdependence of the national economy, Duncan and Lieberson never justify their selection of New Orleans as the benchmark against which all other cities will be measured. Apparently, New Orleans was chosen because of its dubious distinction as one of the few cities that have consistently grown slower than the national rate of urban growth. As such, any city with a sustained rate of population growth that exceeds New Orleans's, will eventually surpass it in total population. But once it has surpassed New Orleans, nothing would prevent that city from continuing to grow rapidly and from continuing to surpass other cities in rank. In other words, Duncan and Lieberson, as well as Schnore, fail to link their dating procedures to the growth history of each city. At best, Schnore attempts to pinpoint the date when each city first attained metropolitan status and presumably entered the "take-off into self-sustained growth," while Duncan and Lieberson never explicitly tie their algorithm to any particular stage of the city's growth trajectory. As a result, none of these authors explains how their dating technique relates to the internal transformations in a city's industrial structure. Hence, it is entirely possible that they will not accurately locate the most dynamic, formative epoch for each city.

Although both dating techniques contain several serious defects, they do provide a foundation for a new dating procedure that conforms to the specific model of urban growth, maturation, and decay outlined previously. Rather than highlighting the decade when a city first attained some critical threshold, we can avoid the ambiguities of the earlier algorithms by focusing on the decade when each city finally ceased growing at an above average rate. By this time, its industrial structure should clearly reflect the specific phase of capital accumulation which dominated its formative era and these characteristics should be indelibly imprinted on its economic base. Any further changes within the local economy should be marginal and not sufficiently strong to alter the city's fundamental characteristics.

Accordingly, this new algorithm calculates urban age by first examining the historical profile of each city's decennial population growth rate and then counting the number of decades that have elapsed since the city's rate of growth last exceeded the national rate of urban growth. By proceeding in this manner, we avoid the problems inherent in the choice of a constant and arbitrary threshold. In addition, this technique applies to all cities irrespective of their size. However, its greatest utility rests with its ability to specify the date when the city's era of greatest internal economic transformation ceased since we are assuming that when a city's population stops growing at an above average rate, its industrial structure has also matured and become relatively quiescent.

After assigning a date to each city, we divided the cities into three groups which correspond to the three major waves of capital accumulation that have transformed the national economy. Mercantile or old cities stopped growing at an above average rate on or before 1870; intermediate or industrial cities had their last decade of above average growth between 1880 and 1930 inclusive; new or postindustrial cities have experienced their last decade of above average growth since 1940.

The Problem of Historical Periodization

The question of historical periodization has been a constant thorn in the side of economic, social, and political historians. Except for those infrequent episodes of dramatic upheaval, historical processes unfold in a slow, evolutionary fashion. Marginal, quantitative alterations in the basic system at first pass by relatively unnoticed and produce only minor effects on the operation of the underlying totality. Eventually, however, the cumulative impact of these minor quantitative changes becomes sufficiently powerful and they alter the physiognomy of the old system. Quantitative alterations, in other words, become qualitative, systemic changes once the pervasive nature of the quantitative changes transforms the essential systemic components. New modes of operation and a new set of governing principles surpersede the old and now outmoded system-defining parameters.

The difficulty associated with historical periodization, therefore, is a function of the process of historical transformation. The historians' task is to replace historical continuity with discontinuity; to recognize at what point the cumulative impact of quantitative changes has produced a qualitative transformation. The difficulty of this task is compounded by two additional elements of complexity. First, qualitative change, by its very nature, is in the eye of the beholder. Numerical variations are easily observed and measured; their significance, unfortunately, is not so easily ascertained. In addition, the recognition of qualitative change requires a broad conceptual focus. Before the historian can state that there has been a transformation in the system, he must have a firm grasp of the system and its essential elements.

Urban historians have grappled with all of these problems and, not surprisingly, they have reached widely divergent conclusions. Their debates run the gamut from the proper scope of urban history to a discussion of the best method for defining relevant periods in urban history.

One of the major debates concerns the scope of urban history—should urban historians be concerned with "problems of the city or problems in the city"? Charles Glaab, one of the leading American urban historians, asks: "Is urban history the history of cities, the history of urbanization, or the history of anything that takes place in an urban setting?"[16] Lampard argues that urban history should be viewed as one dimension of social history and that changes in the urban milieu must be related to changes in social organization: "Urban must signify not subject matter alone but a scheme of conceptualization in much the same way as economic or cultural history."[17] Briggs, however, is totally opposed to this view. According to his perception of the problem, cities are independent entities with histories that do not possess links to the broader social structure:

> The stages of an individual city's history do not really reflect the received divisions of national history. Periods in community history derive from critical turning points within the community itself; it is often useful for limited purposes to regard urban communities as organic entities—developing objective needs and characteristics at different periods of their growth.[18]

The confusion concerning the scope of urban history is reflected in the approaches that various scholars have used to derive a meaningful method of periodization. McKelvey, for instance, while not as extreme as Briggs in his views concerning the autonomy of cities, does argue that periods of urban history should be defined independently of events occurring in the national sphere. Thus he delineates five eras which he claims reflect the "turning points within the community itself"—the colonial city, boom towns (from the colonial era to 1835), Yankee city era (1835-1870), cosmopolitan cities (1870-1915), and the metropolitan era (1915-present).[19]

Borchert's periodization specifically rejects the notion that urban epochs can be defined in terms of a city's internal transformations. According to his perception of the problem, urban history can be understood only when the city's development is tied to the broader changes and transformations in the social system. The variable which he believes captures the essence of these system-defining changes is transportation technology. Thus, he states: "Four epochs in American history can be identified that have been characterized by changes in technology crucial in the location of urban growth and development: (1) Sail-Wagon, 1790-1830; (2) Iron Horse, 1830-1870; (3) Steel Rail, 1870-1920; (4) Auto-Air-Amenity, 1920-."[20]

Lampard offers an analogous periodization scheme that links transportation technologies and the evolution of a national market to the process of urbanization.[21] Lampard's system delineates three broad eras: (1) a period of initial resource exploitation when the major East Coast metropolitan centers organized their respective hinterlands and extended transportation arteries into the frontier. This period extends from the colonial era to the Civil War; (2) a period of "extension of accessibility" which lasted from the Civil War to World War I. This period, based on the development of more efficient transportation technologies, was simply a more refined repetition of the first era; (3) an era of "nationalization" when the final refinements were added to the economy. The result was a national network based on intimate regional interdependence coordinated through the national market.

Pred, however, departs from both schools of periodization—the internal development school and the technology school—in order to define a series of eras that are related to the changing composition of national income. As we saw in Chapter 5, Pred argues that the city-building process was transformed profoundly by the shift from mercantilism to the industrial revolution.[22] Therefore, he hypothesizes that up to 1840, mercantile activities dominated both the national and local economies. After 1860, industrial dynamics replaced mercantilism, while between 1840 and 1860, the economy was in a stage of transition. Unfortunately, Pred's analysis does not extend beyond 1914, so it is difficult to ascertain whether he believes that the industrial revolution has been displaced by a new organizing principle or whether it has continued unchanged through the 1970s.

The preceding analyses, despite their disagreement concerning the timing of the new eras and the forces nurturing each new era, all have one common basis of agreement—every theory assumes that the city passes through each epoch and is radically transformed as one stage gives way to the next. Duncan and Lieberson, however, break with this traditional model and offer a theory of periodization that is sympathetic to the new urban growth process outlined earlier:

> In working through the materials on manufactures in the leading centers, the localization of new lines of manufacture has seemed more salient than the redistribution of traditional lines of manufacture in generating change in the system of major centers. Insofar as this impression is accurate, a center's industrial structure should mirror its growth history.[23]

Thus, instead of offering a theory of periodization, they propose a theory based on the succession of waves of urbanization. The first wave which they term "continental colonialism" conforms closely with Pred's mercantile era and Lampard's period of initial resource exploitation. They suggest that this was followed by the rise of "steam and steel" centers during the industrial revolution. Finally, they postulate a third wave of urban formation based on the "electric-oil-auto" complex.

An Outline for a New Theory of Periodization

The section dealing with the measurement of urban age referred to three distinct periods of city formation: old or mercantile cities were defined as those whose last decade of above-average growth occurred between 1790 and 1870; if a city stopped growing between 1880 and 1930, it was identified as an intermediate or industrial revolution city; and those cities whose last decade of rapid growth occurred during the post-1940 decades were classified as new or Sunbelt cities. Thus, the first two stages of this periodization scheme coincide with Pred's analysis while the last epoch reflects many of the characteristics attributed by Duncan and Lieberson to the electric-oil-auto complex. However, while these periods coincide with respect to function, the dates attributed to each era are at variance with the dates usually assigned to these periods.

This discrepancy is an inherent feature of both the new theory of urban growth and the new method of dating cities presented earlier. Most periodization debates focus on the date when a new era first appeared. For instance, North concludes that "if one were to date the beginning of acceleration in the economy's growth and the years when industrialization began, it would be during the period from 1823-1843."[24] Fogel, however, disputes this hypothesis and argues that the rapid rise in manufacturing output definitely began in the 1820s.[25] Rostow, in turn, places the beginning of the "take-off into self-sustained growth" in 1843.[26] Gallman also argues that it occurred sometime during the 1840s,[27] and Martin dates the beginning of this transformation in the 1850s.[28]

However, for our purposes, this debate is irrelevant. The new theory of urban growth and urban age is not concerned with the birth of an era but rather with the decade when a particular city-building epoch ended. The theory claims that those cities which stopped growing at an above-average rate on or before 1870 will possess an industrial structure that reflects the dominance of mercantile functions. It is entirely possible, and indeed very probable, that sometime before 1870 a new set of cities emerged with an economic base formed during the industrial revolution. But these cities ended their period of rapid growth in the post-1870 era, a decade that was definitely beyond the range of the mercantile epoch. Therefore, they have been classified as intermediate or Industrial Revolution cities.

From this brief discussion, we can derive two general principles of urban historical periodization:

(1) The relevant date for assigning a city to a particular epoch is a function of when that epoch ceased to be the dominant feature of the economy. By this point, the marginal quantitative alterations in the system should have developed sufficient momentum to qualitatively alter the system-defining parameters and governing principles. Those cities that stopped growing before this qualitative transformation will reflect the characteristics typical of the pre-transformation period, those cities that stopped growing in the posttransformation period will reflect the characteristics of the posttransformation epoch. Thus, a city's incipient stage of growth may occur in an earlier period even though its basic characteristics and personality are a function of the dynamic principles associated with a later epoch.

(2) As a corollary to the first point, we can suggest that it is almost impossible to define a clear set of historical periods. In any one particular era, one set of dynamics and organizing principles will dominate the other elements and transform them so that they conform to and are in harmony with the dominant elements. Yet, while these old elements may be subordinate, they are still present and, moreover, a new set of future elements are being generated simultaneously. Thus, a particular epoch is a melange of past, present, and future eras.

A Reconsideration of the Question
of Population Thresholds

Earlier, the population threshold concept was criticized on the grounds that it was ahistorical. As the economy increases in complexity and as technology advances, numerous scholars have shown that a different threshold population would be necessary to provide the minimum support for an industry. However, by relying on a constant threshold despite the secular increase in complexity, Schnore's dating technique implicitly lowered the requirements for metropolitan status and, in essence, devalued the metropolitan concept. Therefore, the growth rate algorithm was suggested as a remedy for this defect. Yet, a cursory examination of the decade by decade rates of national urban growth appears to expose the growth rate technique to the same criticism (Table 6.1). Especially during the last few decades, the national rate of urban growth has fallen dramatically. From 1790 to 1900 it averaged 58.5% per decade. The lowest recorded rate during that period was 31.9% in the 1810-1820 decade. In the twentieth century, however, only the 1910-1920 decade rate of urban growth exceeded the 30% mark, and in the 1940-1970 period, which I have designated as the era of new city formation, the national rate of urban growth averaged only 23.0% per decade. Clearly, these figures indicate that it has become "easier" for a city to grow faster than average and thus "easier" for a city to be classified as new. Thus, both the population threshold and growth rate techniques would appear to suffer from the same malady. Irrespective of which criterion we use to date cities, the standards would appear to have been progressively reduced.

However, a more detailed analysis reveals that this criticism cannot be applied with equal force to the growth rate technique. Although the average rate of urban growth has declined precipitously, if we look at the decennial rate of growth for each city during its last decade of above-average growth, this precipitous drop does not appear (Table 6.2). Except for the

TABLE 6.1   National Rate of Urban Growth, 1790-1970

Decade	Rate	Decade	Rate	Decade	Rate
1790-1800	59.9	1850-1860	75.4	1910-1920	29.0
1800-1810	63.0	1860-1870	59.3	1920-1930	27.5
1810-1820	31.9	1870-1880	42.7	1930-1940	8.0
1820-1830	62.6	1880-1890	56.5	1940-1950	20.6
1830-1840	63.7	1890-1900	36.7	1950-1960	29.3
1840-1850	92.1	1900-1910	39.2	1960-1970	19.2

1820-1830, 1840-1850, and 1850-1860 decades, the average growth rate has remained relatively stable, generally oscillating between 45% and 70%. Thus, while the standard may have depreciated, the performance of each city during its last decade of above-average growth has not experienced any secular depreciation.

Furthermore, it is plausible to argue that the criterion for assigning a city to the 1960-1970 decade is more stringent than the criterion used to assign a city to the 1840-1850 decade. During the early stages of urban growth and development, cities had three sources of population to draw upon—rural residents, immigrants from other countries, and migrants from other urban places. However, during the most recent decades, two of these reservoirs have been relatively dry. As the population has become more urbanized, the supply of rural residents has diminished. In addition, since the 1920s, the flow of legal immigrants has been curtailed drastically. Thus, rapid urban growth can be fueled primarily from one source—residents of established urban places must be lured away from their old homes and induced to settle in a new city. These developments would appear to have dramatically increased the difficulty of sustaining rapid rates of urban growth and made new city formation much closer to a zero sum game. What one city loses in population, its rival gains. This produces regional and intermetropolitan population redistribution, but the new increments to the stock of urban population remain relatively small. Thus, the figures depicting a secular

TABLE 6.2   Average Rate of Growth for Cities During Their Last Decade
of Growth That Exceeds the National Rate of Urban Growth

Decade	Rate	Decade	Rate	Decade	Rate
1790-1800	63.4	1850-1860	205.6	1910-1920	58.3
1800-1810	–	1860-1870	70.8	1920-1930	46.2
1810-1820	–	1870-1880	63.4	1930-1940	15.4
1820-1830	121.9	1880-1890	102.0	1940-1950	48.4
1830-1840	72.0	1890-1900	48.7	1950-1960	60.3
1840-1850	239.9	1900-1910	63.8	1960-1970	48.7

decline in the national rate of urban growth may be sympto-
matic of an increasing threshold and not an indication that the
growth rate dating method applies progressively lower standards.

Empirical Results

In addition to the underlying theoretical and conceptual
differences between the population threshold and growth rate
algorithms, these two dating procedures yield significantly different results when they are both applied to the identical
sample of cities. This section presents some of these empirical
disparities and, in addition, illustrates more vividly the impact
of the different conceptual foundations on the age assigned to
cities.

The sample of cities used in this study comprises all 308
central cities of the nation's 243 Standard Metropolitan Statis-
tical Areas as defined by the Office of Management and Budget
in 1970. As of 1970, 53 of these cities were smaller than 50,000
and the total sample ranges in size from New York City with
7.9 million people to Colonial Heights, Virginia, whose population was only 15,000. However, this sample does not include
every city whose population exceeded 50,000. Certain large
suburban or satellite cities (for example, Cambridge, MA; Yonk-
ers, NY; and Santa Monica, CA) that OMB did not designate as
central cities were excluded. Altogether, 131 suburban cities in

the 50,000-250,000 size range were omitted from the list of central cities, but apparently every city whose population exceeds 250,000 has been automatically defined as a central city by OMB and included in the sample.

Table 6.3 presents the age for all 308 central cities as computed by both dating techniques. According to the Schnore criterion which designates a city as "old" if it reached the 50,000 population mark on or before 1910, there were 102 old cities and 158 new cities. In addition, 48 cities were assigned to the no date category since they have never surpassed the 50,000 threshold level.

Applying the growth rate method to the same sample produced 15 cities whose growth peaked on or before 1870. These cities reached maturity during the first wave of urbanization accompanying the earliest phase of U.S. economic development and, consequently, they have been classified as "old" or "mercantile" cities. The list includes Boston, Harrisburg, Philadelphia, New Haven, New Orleans, Cincinnati, Baltimore, St. Louis, Albany, and New York City. The intermediate or Industrial Revolution category contains 92 cities and includes such major industrial centers as Cleveland, Buffalo, Chicago, Detroit, Jersey City, Newark, Providence, Bridgeport, Dayton, Toledo, and Akron. Finally, 189 cities whose growth peaked on or after 1940 were classified as new cities. Generally, although not exclusively, these are the cities that are located in what is usually referred to as the Sunbelt or southern rim of the United States. In addition, twelve cities whose growth rates never exceeded the national rate of urban growth were placed in the no date category.

These results are summarized in Table 6.4, which presents a frequency distribution of the urban ages computed by both dating methods. The greatest discrepancies occur in the 1940-1970 decades. Schnore only assigned 94 cities (less than one-third) to this period while the growth rate procedure places 176 cities or 57% of the total in these same decades. In addition, whereas Schnore would conclude that the decennial

(text continued on p. 184)

TABLE 6.3   Urban Age for 308 Central Cities

	Population Threshold	Growth Rate
ALABAMA		
Birmingham	1910	1950
Gadsden	1950	1950
Huntsville	1960	1970
Mobile	1910	1960
Montgomery	1930	1950
Tuscaloosa	1950	1960
ARIZONA		
Phoenix	1930	1970
Tucson	1950	1970
ARKANSAS		
Little Rock	1910	1970
Pine Bluff	1970	1970
North Little Rock	1960	1970
CALIFORNIA		
Anaheim	1960	1970
Santa Ana	1950	1970
Garden Grove	1960	1970
Bakersfield	1960	1970
Fresno	1930	1970
Los Angeles	1890	1960
Long Beach	1920	1960
Modesto	1970	1970
Oxnard	1970	1970
Ventura	1970	1970
Sacramento	1920	1970
Salinas	1970	1970
Monterrey	no date	1960
San Bernardino	1950	1960
Riverside	1950	1970
Ontario	no date	1970
San Diego	1920	1970
San Francisco	1860	1950
Oakland	1890	1950
San Jose	1930	1970
Santa Barbara	1960	1970
Santa Rosa	1970	1970
Stockton	1940	1940
Vallejo	1960	1960
Napa	no date	1970

TABLE 6.3   Urban Age for 308 Central Cities (Cont)

	Population Threshold	Growth Rate
COLORADO		
Colorado Springs	1950	1970
Denver	1890	1950
Pueblo	1930	1960
CONNECTICUT		
Bridgeport	1890	1920
Bristol	1970	1970
Danburry	1970	1970
Hartford	1890	1920
New Britain	1920	1920
New Haven	1870	1860
New London	no date	1920
Norwich	no date	1960
Norwalk	1950	1960
Stamford	1940	1950
Waterbury	1900	1910
Washington, DC	1860	1940
DELAWARE		
Wilmington	1890	no date
FLORIDA		
Fort Lauderdale	1960	1970
Hollywood	1970	1970
Gainesville	1970	1970
Miami	1930	1950
Orlando	1950	1960
Pensacola	1960	1960
Tallahassee	1960	1970
Tampa	1920	1960
St. Petersburg	1940	1970
West Palm Beach	1960	1960
Jacksonville	1910	1970
GEORGIA		
Albany	1960	1970
Atlanta	1890	1960
Macon	1920	1970
Savannah	1900	1950
Augusta	1920	1940
Columbus	1940	1970

TABLE 6.3   Urban Age for 308 Central Cities (Cont)

	Population Threshold	Growth Rate
HAWAII		
Honolulu	1910	1950
IDAHO		
Boise	1970	1970
ILLINOIS		
Bloomington	no date	1970
Normal	no date	1970
Champaign	1970	1950
Urbana	no date	1970
Chicago	1860	1900
Moline	no date	1910
Rock Island	1960	1940
Decatur	1930	1930
Peoria	1900	1970
Rockford	1920	1960
East St. Louis	1910	1910
Springfield	1910	1910
INDIANA		
Anderson	1970	1970
Fort Wayne	1910	1930
East Chicago	no date	1930
Gary	1920	1960
Hammond	1930	1950
Indianapolis	1880	1870
Lafayette	no date	1950
West Lafayette	no date	1970
Muncie	1950	1920
South Bend	1910	1930
Terre Haute	1910	1910
IOWA		
Cedar Rapids	1930	1970
Davenport	1920	1940
Des Moines	1890	1940
Dubuque	1960	1860
Council Bluffs	1960	1880
Waterloo	1940	1950
Sioux City	1920	1920

TABLE 6.3   Urban Age for 308 Central Cities (Cont)

	Population Threshold	Growth Rate
KANSAS		
Kansas City	1900	1970
Topeka	1920	1960
Wichita	1910	1960
KENTUCKY		
Lexington	1950	1970
Louisville	1860	1930
Owensboro	1970	1940
LOUISIANA		
Baton Rouge	1950	1950
Lafayette	1970	1970
Lake Charles	1960	1970
Monroe	1960	1960
New Orleans	1840	1840
Shreveport	1930	1950
MAINE		
Auburn	no date	1880
Lewiston	no date	1940
Portland	1900	1900
MARYLAND		
Baltimore	1820	1840
MASSACHUSETTS		
Boston	1830	1800
Brockton	1910	1970
Fichtburg	no date	1900
Leominster	no date	1910
Lawrence	1900	1900
Haverhill	no date	no date
Lowell	1880	1880
New Bedford	1900	1910
Pittsfield	1950	1920
Fall River	1890	1900
Springfield	1900	1920
Chicopee	1960	1920
Holyoke	1910	1890
Worcester	1880	1900

TABLE 6.3   Urban Age for 308 Central Cities (Cont)

	Population Threshold	Growth Rate
MICHIGAN		
Ann Arbor	1960	1970
Bay City	1950	1910
Detroit	1870	1930
Flint	1920	1930
Grand Rapids	1890	1900
Jackson	1950	1920
Kalamazoo	1930	1960
Lansing	1920	1970
Muskegon	no date	1940
Muskegon Heights	no date	1930
Saginaw	1910	1930
MINNESOTA		
Duluth	1900	1910
Moorhead	no date	1970
Minneapolis	1890	1910
St. Paul	1890	1890
Rochester	1970	1970
MISSISSIPPI		
Biloxi	no date	1950
Gulfport	no date	1970
Jackson	1940	1960
MISSOURI		
Columbia	1970	1970
Kansas City	1880	1920
St. Joseph	1890	1900
St. Louis	1850	1870
Springfield	1930	1970
MONTANA		
Billings	1960	1960
Great Falls	1960	1960
NEBRASKA		
Lincoln	1920	1960
Omaha	1890	1920

TABLE 6.3   Urban Age for 308 Central Cities (Cont)

	Population Threshold	Growth Rate
NEVADA		
Las Vegas	1960	1970
Reno	1960	1970
NEW HAMPSHIRE		
Manchester	1900	1850
Nashua	1970	1970
Portsmouth	no date	1960
NEW JERSEY		
Atlantic City	1920	1930
Jersey City	1870	1880
Newark	1860	1910
Paterson	1880	1880
Clifton	1950	1950
Pasaic	1910	1910
Camdem	1890	1880
Trenton	1890	1890
Vineland	no date	1970
Mellville	no date	1970
NEW MEXICO		
Albuquerque	1950	1970
NEW YORK		
Albany	1850	1870
Schenectady	1910	1910
Troy	1880	1840
Binghamton	1920	1920
Buffalo	1860	1900
New York	1800	1830
Rochester	1870	1920
Syracuse	1880	1890
Utica	1900	1930
Rome	1960	1950
NORTH CAROLINA		
Asheville	1930	1930
Charlotte	1930	1970

TABLE 6.3   Urban Age for 308 Central Cities (Cont)

	Population Threshold	Growth Rate
Durham	1930	1970
Fayetteville	1970	1960
Greensboro	1930	1970
Winston-Salem	1930	1970
High Point	1960	1960
Raleigh	1950	1970
Wilmington	no date	1950
NORTH DAKOTA		
Fargo	1970	1940
OHIO		
Akron	1910	1920
Canton	1910	1920
Cleveland	1870	1920
Columbus	1880	1950
Dayton	1890	1930
Hamilton	1930	1930
Middletown	no date	1920
Lima	1950	1920
Lorain	1950	1960
Elyria	1970	1970
Mansfield	1970	1940
Springfield	1920	1920
Steubenville	no date	1910
Youngstown	1910	1930
Warren	1960	1930
Cincinnati	1850	1850
Ashland	no date	1920
Toledo	1880	1920
OKLAHOMA		
Lawton	1950	1970
Oklahoma City	1910	1960
Tulsa	1920	1970
OREGON		
Eugene	1960	1970
Portland	1900	1950
Salem	1970	1970

TABLE 6.3   Urban Age for 308 Central Cities (Cont)

	Population Threshold	Growth Rate
PENNSYLVANIA		
Allentown	1910	1920
Bethlehem	1920	1920
Easton	no date	1900
Altoona	1910	1930
Erie	1900	1920
Harrisburg	1900	1870
Johnstown	1910	1910
Lancaster	1920	no date
Philadelphia	1810	1800
Pittsburgh	1850	1880
Reading	1890	no date
Scranton	1890	1890
Wilkes-Barre	1900	1900
Hazelton	no date	1910
York	1930	1900
RHODE ISLAND		
Providence	1860	1880
Pawtuckett	1910	1900
Warwick	1960	1970
SOUTH CAROLINA		
Charleston	1890	1940
Columbia	1930	1950
Greenville	1950	1950
SOUTH DAKOTA		
Sioux Falls	1950	1950
TENNESSEE		
Chattanooga	1920	1930
Knoxville	1920	1970
Nashville-Davidson	1890	1970
Memphis	1890	1970
TEXAS		
Abilene	1950	1960
Amarillo	1940	1960

TABLE 6.3   Urban Age for 308 Central Cities (Cont)

	Population Threshold	Growth Rate
Austin	1930	1970
Beaumont	1930	1950
Port Arthur	1930	1950
Orange	no date	1950
Brownsville	1970	1960
Harlingen	no date	1960
San Benito	no date	1950
Corpus Christi	1940	1970
Dallas	1910	1970
El Paso	1920	1960
Fort Worth	1910	1950
Galveston	1930	1940
Texas City	no date	1970
Houston	1910	1970
Laredo	1950	1950
Lubbock	1950	1960
McAllen	no date	1960
Pharr	no date	1960
Edinburg	no date	1960
Midland	1960	1960
Odessa	1960	1960
San Antonio	1900	1960
Sherman	no date	1960
Dennison	no date	1960
Tyler	1960	1960
Waco	1930	1950
Wichita Falls	1950	1960
Bryan	no date	1970
College Station	no date	1970
San Angelo	1950	1950
Texarkana	no date	1950
UTAH		
Ogden	1950	1950
Provo	1950	1970
Orem	no date	1970
Salt Lake City	1900	1950
VIRGINIA		
Lynchburg	1960	1940
Newport News	1960	1970

TABLE 6.3   Urban Age for 308 Central Cities (Cont)

	Population Threshold	Growth Rate
Hampton	1960	1970
Petersburg	no date	no date
Colonial Heights	no date	1970
Richmond	1870	1920
Norfolk	1910	1960
Roanoke	1920	1950
WASHINGTON		
Seattle	1900	1950
Everett	1970	1970
Spokane	1910	1950
Tacoma	1910	1950
WEST VIRGINIA		
Charleston	1930	1930
Huntington	1920	1930
Wheeling	1920	1920
Weirton	no date	no date
WISCONSIN		
Appleton	1970	1960
Oshkosh	1970	no date
Superior	no date	no date
Green Bay	1950	1920
Kenosha	1950	1920
La Crosse	1970	1930
Madison	1930	1970
Milwaukee	1870	1900
Racine	1920	1920

NOTE: A no date designation signifies either that the city has never reached a population of 50,000 or that its growth has never exceeded the national rate of urban growth.

pace at which new cities have entered their take-off phase has remained fairly stable since 1890, the growth rate technique suggests that the number of cities reaching the stage of urban maturation has accelerated dramatically during the past several decades.

TABLE 6.4   Frequency Distribution of City Age

	Population Threshold Method		Growth Rate Method	
Decade	Number of Cities	Relative Frequency (percentages)	Number of Cities	Relative Frequency (percentages)
1970	28	9.1	89	28.9
1960	34	11.0	47	15.3
1950	32	10.4	40	13.0
1940	8	2.6	13	4.2
1930	28	9.1	19	6.2
1920	28	9.1	29	9.4
1910	29	9.4	16	5.2
1900	19	6.2	15	4.9
1890	22	7.1	5	1.6
1880	9	2.9	8	2.6
1870	7	2.3	4	1.3
1860	7	2.3	2	.6
1850	4	1.3	2	.6
1840	1	.3	3	1.0
1830	1	.3	2	.6
1820	1	.3	0	0
1810	1	.3	0	0
1800	1	.3	2	.6
no date	48	15.6	12	3.9

These discrepancies result from the different assumptions that form the nucleus of both dating techniques. Since the growth rate method highlights the decade when significant growth ceased and the urban economy stabilized while the threshold algorithm pinpoints the decade of developmental take-off, the former method generally assigns the city to a later decade. On average, the threshold technique dates cities sixteen years earlier than does the growth rate method, but this relationship varies significantly from one developmental epoch to the next. For those cities which stopped growing at an above-average rate on or before 1870, the threshold method assigns a date which is almost 12 years *later* than the date assigned by the growth rate approach. For this early period, it apparently was not at all unusual for a city's growth to slow and for its economy to stabilize before it reached the 50,000 threshold level. In fact, by 1870, only 25 urban places had attained this rather lofty population. As a result, for these cities, Schnore dates their take-off into self-sustained growth after their era of rapid growth had ceased.

After 1870, however, the retardation of urban growth rates occurred after the city had surpassed the 50,000 threshold. Thus, for the 81 intermediate cities whose population eventually exceeded 50,000, the threshold technique assigned a date which was, on average, six years earlier than the date assigned by the growth rate approach. Similarly, the 160 cities which were placed in the new city category and which had exceeded the 50,000 mark were assigned a date that was 23 years earlier than the growth rate date.

These observations provide additional evidence to support the claim that Schnore's use of an absolute, temporally constant threshold level ignores the relationship between the increasing technological sophistication of the national economy and the rising threshold required to profitably support an industry. During the mercantile phase of capital accumulation and urban development, the industrial technology was comparatively simple. Consequently, a relatively small city could generate sufficient localization and urbanization economies, and, as a result, many of the nation's oldest cities stopped growing at an above-average rate more than one decade before they reached the 50,000 population level. But as the national economy continued to evolve, mechanization and mass production replaced the craft-based manufacturing activities of the earlier epoch. Not surprisingly, this raised the minimum threshold and caused many industrial cities to mature and stabilize after they exceeded Schnore's critical population level. In the most recent wave of urban development, these disparities have grown even wider as the increased technological sophistication produced a greater difference between the decade when a city first attained metropolitan status and the decade when its industrial structure began to ossify.

Conclusion

How can this new dating algorithm improve our understanding of urban history and the economic forces promoting urban growth, maturation, and decay? First, it must be emphasized that all dating schemes are merely tools. They cannot substitute for careful empirical and historical research. But if they are properly constructed, these tools can indicate some fruitful areas of inquiry. In particular, the growth rate algorithm suggests that the industrial growth profile of each specific city would be one useful avenue of investigation.

If we accept the assertion that the growth or lack of growth in the local economy is the primary factor dividing cities into distinct categories, then a relevant measure of urban age must not only focus on this variable, it must also provide some clues as to the cause of this disparate performance. The 50,000 threshold technique clearly fails to satisfy this requirement. The growth rate algorithm, however, focuses on the relative maturity of each local economy and proposes to date cities according to the decade when their local industrial base ossified and became relatively impervious to the new activities spawned by later phases of capital accumulation. The twin concepts of industrial maturity and developmental barriers discussed earlier, when coupled with the new measure of urban age, will illuminate some of the problems plaguing the older cities and will also suggest specific areas where historical analysis can be most effective.

For example, the growth rate dating procedure stratifies cities on the basis of the developmental epoch that produced the greatest internal transformation in the local economy. Consequently, each city can be classified in terms of those industries that have stamped their imprint on the personality of its industrial base. Since the loss of these industries and the in-

ability to generate sufficient replacements have been hypothesized to be the major cause of their economic distress, economic
and historical analysis must focus on those developmental barriers that prevent cities from altering their basic industrial
characteristics. The growth rate dating procedure by itself cannot offer precise analytic techniques to accomplish these goals.
But in contrast to the other dating algorithms, it can help to
specify the fundamental problem. Also, it can provide an index
of the relative maturity of various urban economies. If it is
utilized in this fashion, it can ensure that our historically based
empirical tools bear some correspondence to concrete historical
processes.

NOTES

1. For an analysis of British and German economic development during the
nineteenth century and Germany's drive to overtake Britain's early lead, see Walt W.
Rostow, *The World Economy: History and Prospect* (Austin: Univ. of Texas Press,
1978); and Thorstein Veblen, *Imperial Germany and the Industrial Revolution* (New
York: Viking, 1939).

2. Edgar Hoover, "Pittsburgh Takes Stock of Itself," in Benjamin Chinitz (ed.),
City and Suburb (Englewood Cliffs, NJ: Prentice-Hall, 1964): 57.

3. "Pittsburgh, Revamped and Revitalized, Sheds Its Steel Town Image," *New
York Times* (April 16, 1977): 27.

4. See Glenn McLaughlin, *Growth of American Manufacturing Areas* (Pittsburgh: Univ. of Pittsburgh Press, 1938); Carl Madden, "Some Temporal Aspects of
the Growth of Cities in the United States," *Economic Development and Cultural
Change* 6, 2 (1958): 143-170; and Beverly Duncan and Stanley Lieberson, *Metropolis
and Region in Transition* (Beverly Hills: Sage Publications, 1970).

5. For an analysis of urban renaissance and gentrification in the Northeast, see
T. D. Allman, "The Urban Crisis Leaves Town and Moves to the Suburbs," *Harpers*
(December 1978): 41-56; "Urban Renaissance: The Reality Beneath the Glitter,"
The Progressive (January 1979): 26-47; Blake Fleetwood, "The New Elite and an
Urban Renaissance," *New York Times Magazine* (January 14, 1979): 16-22, 26,
34-35; and David C. Perry and Alfred J. Watkins, "The Urban Renaissance for
Business," *The Nation* (March 1, 1980): 236-239.

6. The analysis of developmental barriers presented in this chapter highlights the
product life cycle constraints that inhibit continuous rapid growth on the basis of an
unchanging set of economic activities. Gordon emphasizes the importance of a

different, but complementary, set of internally generated pressures that eventually emerge as developmental barriers. From his perspective, capitalists must strive toward two, often contradictory, goals. First, they try to maximize their quantitative efficiency, defined as the highest possible output for a given set of factor inputs. In addition, they try to survive and prosper within the context of an economic system predicated upon the existence of an antagonistic set of class relationships. When these antagonisms reach a crisis pitch, the social control or qualitative efficiency of the production process has hit a developmental barrier, which, Gordon argues, has usually been eliminated by altering the industrial location pattern and moving from one method of capital accumulation to a new and'more "opaque" stage. According to Gordon, the adjustments inspired by these periodic reductions in qualitative efficiency are a major factor behind the correlation between different stages of capital accumulation and different phases of urban development as well as the propensity for new industries to locate in new cities. See David M. Gordon, "Class Struggle and the Stages of American Urban Development," in David C. Perry and Alfred J. Watkins, (eds.), *The Rise of the Sunbelt Cities* (Beverly Hills: Sage Publications, 1977): 55-82.

7. See Arthur F. Burns, *Production Trends in the United States Since 1870* (New York: National Bureau of Economic Research, 1934): 120-173.

8. Ibid.: 141.

9. Ibid.: 152-153.

10. Ibid.: 160.

11. Ibid.: 170.

12. See Leo Schnore, "City Suburban Income Differentials in Metropolitan Areas," *American Sociological Review* 27, 2 (1962): 252-255; and "Urban Structure and Suburban Selectivity," *Demography* 1, 1 (1964): 164-176.

13. Allen Pred, *The Spatial Dynamics of U.S. Urban Industrial Growth, 1800-1914* (Cambridge, MA: MIT Press, 1966): 50.

14. See John Borchert, "American Metropolitan Evolution," *Geographical Review* 57, 4 (1967): 301-332; and Fred Lukerman, "Empirical Expressions of Nodality and Hierarchy in a Circulation Manifold," *East Lakes Geographer* 2, 1 (1966): 17-44.

15. Duncan and Lieberson, op. cit.

16. Charles Glaab, "The Historian and the American City: A Bibliographic Survey," in Philip Hauser and Leo Schnore (eds.), *The Study of Urbanization* (New York: Macmillan, 1965): 56.

17. Eric Lampard, quoted in Glaab, op. cit.: 57.

18. Asa Briggs, quoted in Glaab, op. cit.: 61.

19. Blake McKelvey, quoted in Glaab, op. cit.: 63.

20. Borchert, op. cit.: 38. For a more extensive discussion of the relationship between transport technology and urban evolution, see James E. Vance, Jr., "Labor Shed, Employment Field, and Dynamic Analysis in Urban Geography," *Economic Geography* 36, 3 (1960): 189-220.

21. Eric E. Lampard, "Regional Economic Development, 1870-1950," in Harvey Perloff et al., *Regions, Resources, and Economic Growth* (Baltimore: Johns Hopkins Univ. Press, 1960): 107-292.

22. Pred, op. cit.

23. Duncan and Lieberson, op. cit.: 178.

24. Douglas C. North, *The Economic Growth of the United States, 1790-1860* (Englewood Cliffs, NJ: Prentice-Hall, 1961): 48.

25. Robert W. Fogel, *Railroads in American Economic Growth: Essays in Econometric History* (Baltimore: Johns Hopkins Univ. Press, 1964).

26. Walt W. Rostow, *The Stages of Economic Growth* (Cambridge, MA: Cambridge Univ. Press, 1960).

27. Robert E. Gallman, "Commodity Output, 1839-1899," in William N. Parker (ed.), *Trends in the American Economy in the Nineteenth Century* (Princeton, NJ: National Bureau of Economic Research, 1960): 13-71.

28. Robert F. Martin, *National Income of the United States, 1799-1938* (New York: National Bureau of Economic Research, 1939).

Chapter 7

ECONOMIC EVOLUTION AND
U.S. URBAN DEVELOPMENT

In this chapter, the preceding discussion of uneven urban development and urban age will be used as a guide for interpreting the history of the evolution of the U.S. system of cities. Four salient features of each developmental epoch will be discussed: the nature and impact of the epoch defining activities, the barriers erected by the leading cities to ensure that their rivals would remain in a subordinate position, the internal contradictions which signified the end of a particular phase of capital accumulation, and the opportunities for a new set of cities to emerge based upon new techniques of capital accumulation. However, one word of caution is necessary before we proceed with the historical analysis of each epoch. These vignettes are not intended to provide exhaustive and definitive case histories either of specific cities or eras. Rather, they are meant to be suggestive. Hopefully, they will highlight some of the major variables and processes that a full-scale historical investigation should document in greater detail. Thus, they are presented as tentative beginnings, not as conclusive historical pronouncements.

URBAN GROWTH AND MERCANTILE ACCUMULATION

The history of U.S. urbanization is, in great measure, also the history of the development and evolution of U.S. capitalism. Capitalism, however, did not simply arise out of thin air nor did capitalist institutions immediately appear in their fully matured form. Instead, this mode of social and economic organization had to be meticulously constructed. Of paramount importance was the elimination of the self-sufficient frontier economy and its replacement with a commercial agricultural system. During the mercantile phase of capital accumulation, those cities that spearheaded the assault on this barrier emerged as the leading metropolitan centers controlling the pace of national development.

Although the pre-1870 urban population was a relatively small percentage of the total population, the influence of these urban centers greatly exceeded their proportion of the national population. In 1800 only six centers had populations exceeding 8,000, the population used at the time to distinguish between urban and rural areas. Using the present population threshold of 2,500 people, there were 33 urban places in 1800 housing 6.1% of the national population. By 1840, the number of urban places had increased to 131 but the share of the population residing in urban areas was still only 10.8%. Finally, in 1860, toward the end of the mercantile period, there were 392 urban areas containing 19.8% of the total population. In 60 years, the urban share of the population had increased by more than 300%. Only during the 1810-1820 decade did the rate of urban growth fail to exceed the rate of total population growth.

Despite this rapid increase in the number of urban places, we do not have to study every city in order to understand the relationship between urban growth and national economic development. Instead, since the cities at the top of the urban hierarchy shaped the nation's economic destiny, an analysis of a few key metropolitan centers will elucidate most of the salient trends and patterns.

Table 7.1 traces the population growth of the 10 largest cities as of 1860. Although all 10 cities grew rapidly during the mercantile era, wide disparities exist between the growth rates of different cities and also between the growth rate of the same city during different decades. Philadelphia and Boston, for example, were two of the slowest growing cities during this era. Their rate of population growth never exceeded the national rate of urban population growth. New York City surpassed this rate only during the 1790-1800 and 1820-1830 decades. Baltimore stopped growing faster than the national urban average in 1820, Cincinnati in 1850, St. Louis in 1870, and New Orleans in 1840. More importantly, these mercantile centers were just completing their era of rapid growth and they occupied the top seven positions in the urban hierarchy. The remaining three cities as well as the ten next largest—Louisville, Albany, Washington, DC, San Francisco, Providence, Pittsburgh, Rochester, Detroit, Milwaukee, and Cleveland—all stopped growing faster than the national average urban growth rate in the decades after 1870.[1]

In many cases, a city's growth spurt can be attributed to a specific event. For example, New York's spurt in the 1820-1830 decade corresponds to the opening of the Erie Canal. Philadelphia and Boston, which both experienced lagging population increases, also lagged in the race to capture a significant share of the growing hinterland trade. Chicago began to boom during the 1840s after the construction of a canal connecting Lake Michigan to a tributary of the Mississippi River and the first links in the rail network that would eventually convert Chicago into the transportation hub of the Midwest. Finally, Cincinnati's and St. Louis's decade of most rapid population growth coincides with the settlement of the Ohio and Mississippi valleys and the emergence of a prosperous hinterland.

Thus, by 1870 the growth rates of the seven largest cities had all peaked and from then on they were below the national average. The next 13 cities in the urban hierarchy followed a different trajectory since their economic foundation rested on

TABLE 7.1 Population and Rate of Population Growth for the Largest 10 Cities in 1860; 1800-1860 (population in thousands)

		1800	1810	1820	1830	1840	1850	1860
New York[a]	Pop.	63.7	107.7	130.8	217.8	348.9	612.3	1072.2
	% Change	82.7	59.3	28.3	63.7	54.4	64.9	57.8
Philadelphia[b]	Pop.	69.4	91.8	112.7	161.4	220.4	340.0	562.5
	% Change	44.5	30.3	18.8	26.1	16.4	29.6	65.9
Baltimore	Pop.	26.1	35.5	62.7	80.6	102.1	169.0	212.4
	% Change	96.4	75.6	34.8	28.5	26.9	65.2	25.7
Boston	Pop.	24.9	33.2	43.2	61.3	93.3	136.8	177.8
	% Change	36.1	35.5	28.1	41.8	52.1	46.6	29.9
New Orleans	Pop.		17.2	27.1	46.3	102.1	116.3	168.6
	% Change			57.6	69.6	121.8	13.9	44.9
Cincinnati	Pop.		2.5	9.6	24.8	46.3	115.4	161.0
	% Change			279.6	157.5	86.6	149.1	39.5
St. Louis	Pop.				4.9	16.4	77.8	160.7
	% Change					230.9	372.8	106.5
Chicago	Pop.					4.8	29.9	109.2
	% Change						570.3	274.4
Buffalo	Pop.		1.5	2.0	8.6	18.2	42.2	81.1
	% Change			38.9	313.7	110.1	132.0	92.0
Newark	Pop.				10.9	17.2	38.8	71.9
	% Change					57.9	125.0	85.0

SOURCE:: U.S. Census data.
a. Figures for New York City represent the summation of population and population changes for both New York City and Brooklyn. Brooklyn was an independent city until 1898 and was the fourth largest urban area until its merger with New York.
b. The 1850-1860 growth rate is the result of the 1854 expansion of the Philadelphia boundaries due to an extensive annexation program.

industrial rather than mercantile accumulation. Yet despite their eventual emergence as industrial cities, many began life as mercantile outposts. Albany's rise may be attributed to the Erie Canal, while San Francisco owed her prominence to the discovery of gold and its location as the eastern terminus for the China and Far East trade. Pittsburgh and Rochester may also trace their early prominence to the construction of internal improvements and other mercantile activities. Similarly, Detroit, Milwaukee, and Cleveland are all located on the Great Lakes and as a result, served as transhipment points. However, for the most part (San Francisco being a clear exception), these cities were never considered to be principal trading depots. Instead, by the time their growth rates slowed, they possessed a large core of resource-oriented manufacturing activities. The Industrial Revolution, rather than mercantile accumulation, spurred the growth of this group.

The Process of Mercantile Accumulation

Two immediate obstacles—one attitudinal and the other physical—blocked the path of mercantile accumulation. With respect to the psychological barrier, contemporary observers noted that farmers could not be induced to produce a surplus above and beyond their own subsistence requirements unless markets were available. As early as 1810, Congressman David Porter of New York remarked:

The single circumstance of want of a market is already beginning to produce the most disastrous effect, not only on industry, but on the morals of the inhabitants. Such is the fertility of their land that one-half their time spent in labor is sufficient to produce every article which their farms are capable of yielding, in sufficient quantities for their own consumption, and there is nothing to incite them to produce more. They are therefore, naturally led to spend the other part of their time in idleness and dissipation. Their increase in numbers far from encourage them to become manufacturers for themselves, but put to a greater distance the time when . . . they submit to the labor and confinement of manufacturers.[2]

Although these psychological attitudes were anathema to mercantile interests, they could not be altered as long as the available transport network prevented the establishment of profitable commercial links with the interior. In other words, irrespective of their psychological predisposition, the crude and primitive transportation facilities prevented farmers from either marketing a cash crop or consuming the wares sold by urban merchants.

The significance of this transport barrier can be documented by examining the freight charges preceding the vast program of internal improvements. In 1816, before the beginning of work on the Erie Canal, the cost of transporting one ton of goods from Europe to New York was $9.00. This same nine dollars would have paid for the transportation of one ton of freight 30 miles over the primitive turnpike system then in existence.[3] European goods destined for Pittsburgh were shipped inland via New Orleans and the Mississippi River rather than overland through one of the East Coast ports. Farm produce from the Midwest required an equally roundabout journey to market. Otherwise, overland freight charges would absorb the entire selling price. According to one economic historian,

> In 1816 wheat and corn were selling at relatively high prices in Philadelphia, averaging about $1.94 and $1.13 respectively, a bushel. With costs for teaming at 30 cents a ton mile, the mere charge for carting wheat to Philadelphia equalled its whole selling price if it were drawn 218 miles; for corn this was true for a distance of 135 miles. The month before the Erie Canal was authorized—March, 1817—a committee of the New York State Legislature found that the cost of transportation from Buffalo to New York City was three times the market value of wheat in New York City, six times that of corn, and twelve times that of oats.[4]

As a result, neither high value manufactured goods now low value, bulky farm produce could be sold at a profit under the prevailing system of freight rates.

Not only were transport costs prohibitive, but the time required for hauling goods overland was another serious obstacle blocking the establishment of intimate commercial ties. For instance, it required at least 50 days to ship commodities from Cincinnati to New York. A lag of this duration between shipment and arrival at the final destination meant that inland merchants and farmers could never be sure of the price and market situation. In a period of somewhat less than two months the market could become glutted and an entire crop would be sold at a loss. The risks were just too great to encourage regular commercial connections.

Because of these physical barriers, most of the hinterland commerce was controlled by New Orleans merchants. A symbiotic relationship developed between the West and the South, aided and abetted by those cities that were strategically situated along the major waterways. Cities sprang up along the Ohio, Mississippi, and Missouri rivers wherever rapids and water-falls created break-in-bulk points that required special cargo handling. Also, the junctions of major rivers provided another excellent urban location. Commodities arriving from many directions would be shipped to these junctions, where they were then unloaded and consolidated with other cargoes headed for the same destination. Pittsburgh, Louisville, St. Louis, Cincinnati, and New Orleans were all founded as *entrepot* mercantile centers, and their growth may be directly linked to the volume of hinterland commodities which passed through their ports.[5]
If left unchecked, these southerly trade flows would foster the development of western and southern cities and reduce the prosperity of the East Coast port cities. However, the East Coast merchants were not content to sit by idly while this lucrative trade slipped from their grasp. Instead, they built a comprehensive network of canals and railroads that reduced freight charges and wrenched trade flows away from New Orleans.

However, before this transportation barrier could be eliminated, urban merchants had to surmount an equally serious financial barrier. Despite the favorable impact of canals, turnpikes, and railroads, the mercantile community was reluctant to commit its own capital to internal improvement projects.

Instead, merchants demanded and received public financing from the federal, state, and local treasuries.[6]

Frequently, the promoters of internal improvements justified their departure from laissez-faire by claiming that the resulting local prosperity would benefit the entire community. Therefore, the merchants argued, the cost of these projects should be shared by everyone:

> There was the more or less conscious adoption of metropolitan goals: the delineation of hoped for trading areas and the elaboration of strategies to gain them. In this process some kind of public consensus had to be achieved if only because the transportation schemes required considerable public financing and other legislation. Consequently notions of the "general interest" emerged in debates about the proper competitive course to pursue; the railroad or the canal was desired, or was talked about as desired, not just by this or that group of aggressive Baltimore or Philadelphia businessmen but by "Baltimore" or "Philadelphia."[7]

Purchasing the stocks and bonds issued by internal improvement corporations was the most direct source of public financing. Cranmer estimates that between 1817 and 1860, $194 million were invested in the canal system. More than 60% of these funds were supplied by the public sector.[8] In the West, the proportion of public financing was even greater. In that region, government funds provided $19.8 million or 90% of the total capital invested in canals. However, these figures generally underestimate the real significance of the public investment. In many cases, when private individuals purchased stock, the canal companies did not receive cash. Instead, bank notes that were trading at a large discount were accepted at face value. Also, private investors could pledge future dividends in return for their stock. Since these loopholes were not available to the public sector, the proportion of cash supplied by public agencies greatly exceeded the book value of the stocks and bonds which they purchased.

In addition to stock purchases, public land grants were used as collateral for loans from the private sector.[9] Since the price of land adjacent to the canal was destined to rise after the canal began to operate, these parcels could then be sold to raise funds and retire the construction debt. In Illinois, for example, land grants provided more than 90% of the capital for the construction of the Illinois and Michigan Canal. Toll revenues accounted for the balance. In many other instances, public credit supplemented the meager borrowing capacity of the canal companies. Under this arrangement, the states would issue special bonds to European creditors and give the proceeds to canal companies. In return, the canal companies reserved a portion of their toll revenues for debt retirement. As a result of this wide-spread practice, new state indebtedness rose from $13 million in the period from 1820-1824 to $108 million in the years 1835-1837.[10] By the early 1840s, the states had created "a funded debt of more than $200,000,000—a larger debt than the federal government had ever owed, and the first large debt created by the government of any country for purely industrial purposes."[11]

With this concerted effort to construct canals and railroads, freight rates plummeted and trade patterns shifted dramatically. As early as 1851, one observer, J.D.B. DeBow, remarked that northern transportation systems had "rolled back the mighty tide of the Mississippi and its ten thousand tributary streams until their mouth, practically and commercially, is more at New York and Boston than at New Orleans."[12]

But they did more than roll back the tide. By inhibiting southern growth, the new transport network fostered uneven development and allowed northern prosperity to induce southern poverty. Fishlow, for example, reports that as early as 1839, the bulk of western produce was shipped directly to the major East Coast port cities and was bypassing New Orleans. The decline of New Orleans as a transshipment center proceeded in pace with the completion of additional links in the internal improvement system.

The proportion of flour flowing eastward or northward from Cincinnati increased from 3 percent in the early 1850s to 90 percent in

1860; similarly for pork, there was a shift from 7 percent to 42 percent. . . . Almost twice as much flour, eight times as much pork and bacon, twice as much lard, and three times as much of both corn and beef were exported from New Orleans in 1846-1849 than in 1858-1861.[13]

Trade flows along the Erie Canal corroborate Fishlow's assessment. In 1835, eastbound flour and what shipments amounted to only 268,000 barrels. By 1840, the shipments exceeded 1,000,000 barrels and by 1860, 4,344,000 barrels. By 1838, flour receipts at Buffalo exceeded those at New Orleans.

Thus, while New Orleans did not suffer an absolute decline as a mercantile center, its growth had begun to wane, and with the completion of the canal system, the bulk of its exports consisted of cotton. The city was one of the first southern centers to fall prey to an early round of divergent, uneven development as it lost the battle for control of the hinterland to the emerging mercantile centers of the Northeast. The canals had broken the barrier of North-South waterways, and New Orleans, once the beneficiary of these barriers, was now trapped by their elimination.

Despite southern attempts to retaliate with the construction of its own publically supported internal improvements, the South was fighting a losing battle.[14] The trade routes had been permanently altered, and the patterns of divergent development that would characterize southern economic history for the next 100 years had been firmly established. To many contemporary observers it appeared that southern wealth was the source of northern profits.[15] Southern complaints were loud and vociferous but to no avail. One southern writer, upset over the financial supremacy of the East Coast port cities, lamented:

Last autumn the rich regions of Ohio, Indiana and Illinois were flooded with banknotes of the eastern states, advanced by the New York houses on produce to be shipped by them by way of the canals in the spring. These moneyed facilities enable the packer, miller, and speculator to hold onto their produce until the opening of navigation in the spring and they are no longer obliged as formally, to hurry off their shipments during the winter by way of New Orleans in order to realize funds by drafts on their shipments. The banking facilities of the East are doing so much to draw trade from us as the canals and railways which eastern capital is constructing.[16]

An even more plaintive cry was raised by another Southerner: "The South thus stands in the attitude of feeding from her own bosom a vast population of merchants, shipowners, capitalists, and others who, without the claims of progeny, drink up the lifeblood of her trade."[17]

Indeed, in the period immediately preceding the Civil War, urban mercantile interests had become so adept at controlling and financing southern trade that they pocketed 42 cents from each dollar of final sales.[18] Factors, acting as the agents of urban merchants, appeared in the major market centers to purchase southern crops and arrange for their shipment. Inspectors, insurance agents, transport agents, and warehouse agents soon dominated the urban occupation structure and accounted for a major proportion of the total urban income. Most of these revenues were obtained at the expense of southern and western farmers and provided a major barrier to their prosperity. Funds were drained from the agricultural regions in order to enrich the urban mercantile economies of the East. According to one southern planter, "The steamer charges a dollar a bale. The sampler, weigher, drayman, piccory, warehouse, and pressman and brokers all have a snug percent. The factor has on average, a dollar a bale for selling . . . and all that comes out of your pocket and mine."[19]

In conclusion, at the beginning of the mercantile era, a physical barrier blocked northern economic development. Those cities that were most adept at overcoming this obstacle soon emerged as the major mercantile centers of the nation. By directing trade flows through their borders, these cities inaugurated a process of cumulative and self-reinforcing growth fueled by the commercial profits that they siphoned from the agrarian regions. But with the passage of time, this matrix of mercantile activities lost its dynamic quality. The impact of this event profoundly influenced the development prospects in both the major mercantile cities and the subordinate urban outposts.

For the latter group of cities, the closing of the mercantile phase of capital accumulation meant that commercial functions were no longer capable of boosting them into the ranks of major metropolitan centers. Unless they could overcome this barrier by proceeding in a new fashion, they would be forever doomed to a subordinate status. In the major mercantile centers, the waning of mercantile-based growth had equally ominous consequences. During the mercantile era, these cities had risen to their present dominant status by expanding their hinterland. But once each city's hinterland was firmly defined and the frontier partitioned among the major centers, growth based upon hinterland expansion was relatively difficult. Although it was unlikely that these cities would die, their potential for continued rapid growth based upon old techniques was clearly limited.

In both groups of cities, the termination of the mercantile phase of development was a function of mercantilism's previous success. By the end of this period, the physical isolation of the frontier was over, a complex network of commercial ties linked the agrarian sectors with the mercantile cities of the East Coast and Europe, a national market had been created, and trade patterns had been successfully diverted from New Orleans. As a result, the preconditions for a successful foray into industrial methods of capital accumulation were in place. The economy was poised for a new round of economic development based upon new ideas and new techniques. How the two groups of cities would deal with these barriers/opportunities would determine the course of uneven development during the industrial phase of economic development.

URBAN GROWTH AND INDUSTRIAL ACCUMULATION

The Growth of Manufacturing

Although there has been some dispute concerning the date that the U.S. economy embarked upon the Industrial Revolution, the influence of this shift on the urban system has been recognized for over a century. As far back as 1880, the Census Bureau declared that it is difficult to ascertain

in what proportion the growth of cities of the country as a body, has been due to commercial and in what proportion to industrial forces, . . . but I conceive that no one will hesitate to assent to the proposition that the growth of cities of the U.S. since 1850 has been due in far greater measure to their development as manufacturing centers than to their increased business as centers for the distribution of commercial production.[20]

The Census Bureau was not alone in its assessment. Many urban entrepreneurs and influential businessmen also recognized that the matrix of city-building activities had shifted to manufacturing. Kirkland, for example, quotes one urban entrepreneur who declared, "The encouragement of the manufacturing industries is the most direct and most lucrative method of increasing the wealth of a community."[21] The editor of the Cleveland *Leader* echoed these sentiments when he remarked, "No thinking man with capital will stop here when we have only commerce to sustain us. A manufacturing town gives a man full scope for his ambitions."[22] The President of the Los Angeles Chamber of Commerce called for a program of "Balanced Prosperity" because, "It is our opinion that only by laying a high industrial foundation to our rapid growth can we hope to bring about a stabilized prosperity."[23]

The hue and cry for the addition of a manufacturing base to buttress the old mercantile foundation was well founded. Not only had manufacturing activities grown dramatically, but the most rapid growth and the most dynamic industries were concentrated largely in the major urban centers. Any city that could capture a significant share of this new activity could expect rapid growth and "stabilized prosperity."

In 1849, the United States was a relatively unindustrialized nation. The number of "gainful workers" totaled 7.7 million, but only 957,059, or 11.6% were employed in manufacturing (Table 7.2). The total value of manufacturing products was

TABLE 7.2 Manufacturing Activities in the United States for Selected Years, 1849-1929

Year	Manufacturing Wage Earners	Total Number of Gainful Workers (thousands)	Total Value of Product	Value Added by Manufacturing
1849	957,059	7,697	1,019,106,616	463,982,734
1859	1,311,246	10,533	1,885,861,676	854,256,584
1869	2,053,996	12,925	3,385,860,354	1,395,118,560
1879	2,732,595	17,392	5,369,579,191	1,972,755,642
1889	4,251,535	23,318	9,372,378,843	4,210,364,965
1899[a]	5,306,143	29,073	13,000,149,159	5,656,521,284
1899[b]	4,712,763	29,073	11,406,926,701	4,831,075,210
1909	6,615,046	37,371	20,672,051,870	8,529,260,992
1919	9,000,059	42,434	62,041,795,316	24,809,092,926
1929	8,838,743	48,830	70,434,863,443	31,885,283,711

SOURCES: For gainful workers — U.S. Bureau of the Census, *Historical Statistics of the United States, Colonial Times to 1970*, Bicentennial Edition, Part 1 (Washington, DC: U.S. Government Printing Office, 1975): 138. For all other figures — Fifteenth Census of the United States, *Manufactures: 1929*, Volume III, Reports by States (Washington, DC: U.S. Government Printing Office, 1933): Table 1.

a. Figures are for factory, hand, and neighborhood industries.
b. Figures are for factories, excluding hand and neighborhood industries.

slightly greater than one billion dollars, and the value added was less than half that amount.

Within a few years this situation changed dramatically. By 1869, the number of manufacturing workers had more than doubled, while value added and the total value of product had tripled. Between 1869 and 1889 the story repeated itself— manufacturing workers had again doubled and value added and total value of product tripled. From 1869 to 1929, the period that includes the second phase of urban development, the total number of manufacturing workers increased by 440%, total value of product rose by 2,100%, and value added shot ahead by 2,446%.

The lion's share of this growth occurred in the major urban areas. For example, between 1860 and 1890, the percentage of total manufacturing employment concentrated in the largest 25 industrial counties rose from 30.2% to 42.4%. Besides this employment concentration, the evidence suggests that the most advanced and sophisticated plants in each industry were located primarily in the largest industrial centers (Table 7.3 and Table 7.4). For every variable listed in Table 7.3, the values for the 165 principal cities were at least 50% greater than the value for the United States excluding these 165 cities. The most capital-intensive operations, employing the greatest number of workers per establishment, and paying the highest annual wage were all located in major urban areas. When the total manufacturing data are disaggregated by industry, the same pattern emerges. In only seven industries was there a higher value of capital per establishment in the remainder of the United States than in the principal cities.

However, despite the rapid growth of manufacturing activities and their concentration in the major urban centers, the rise of industrial accumulation did not alter the economic base of every city. Many of the dominant mercantile centers retained their old economic base. Since mercantile accumulation had lost its dynamic attributes, mercantile cities grew at below-average rates. In contrast to the mercantile cities, a group of subordinate mercantile centers seized the opportunity offered by industrial accumulation. Not surprisingly, between 1880 and 1930 this latter group contained the fastest-growing, most prosperous cities.

What caused these divergent patterns of development? What barriers prevented the mercantile cities from updating their economic base? Why could the newly emerging industrial cities break the barriers that had throttled the growth of the leading mercantile centers? To answer these questions, we must consider each group of cities separately.

Mercantile Cities and Industrial Accumulation

The failure of the dominant mercantile elites to prosper from industrial accumulation has received considerable attention by economic historians. Mantoux, for example, argues that inertia is a major concept that must be included in any analysis of economic dynamics. Once a group of economic actors become

TABLE 7.3   Average Capital, Miscellaneous Expenses, Employees, Wages,
Cost of Materials, and Value of Product per Establishment,
and Average Annual Earnings per Employee for the United
States, the 165 Principal Cities, and the United States
Exclusive of the 165 Cities, 1890

Item	United States	165 Principal Cities	United States Exclusive of 165 Principal Cities
Average capital per establishment	18,359	21,470	14,937
Average miscellaneous expenses per establishment	1,776	2,443	1,042
Average number of employees per establishment	13.26	15.62	10.66
Average wages per establishment	6,424	8,420	4,228
Average annual earnings per employee	484	539	396
Average cost of materials per establishment	14,523	18,067	10,627
Average value of products per establishment	26,370	33,727	18,279

SOURCE: Eleventh Census of the United States, *Report on Manufacturing Industries: 1890*, Part II, *Statistics of Cities* (Washington DC: U.S. Government Printing Office, 1895): XI.

enamored of one set of behavior patterns and mode of capital accumulation, they become reluctant to abandon the proven, effective methods for new and uncharted techniques:

We must also reckon with the difficulties involved in changing from one economic system to another, even when the latter appears to be the natural outcome of the former. Between their logical relationship and the actual change from one to the other, there is room for every kind of resistance which self interest and prejudice can suggest. The merchant manufacturers, accustomed as they were to the methods their fathers had used before, found it hard to change. The outlay in equipment and building demanded by a factory frightened them. Why should they incur such heavy charges when they could, or thought they could, earn just as much with less expense and fewer risks. The distance between them and the captains of industry was not great, but they never thought it worth their while to cover it. They soon had to bear the consequences of their timidity.[24]

TABLE 7.4   Number of Establishments, Average Capital per
Establishment, and Average Capital Required to Produce a
Product Valued at $100 in the 165 Principal Cities and the
United States Exclusive of These Cities for 25 Selected
Industries, 1890

	165 Principal Cities		
Industry	Number of Establishments	Average Capital per Establishment	Average Amount of Capital Required for a Product Valued at $100
Agricultural implements	195	429,685	189.28
Boots and shoes	1,269	41,708	41.87
Brass cuttings and brass finishing	408	39,494	77.85
Chemicals	356	108,964	82.44
Clothing, men's	4,629	26,819	51.13
Clothing, women's	1,199	17,481	128.38
Dyeing and finishing textiles	191	103,826	122.71
Flour and grist mill products	608	92,628	34.46
Foundry and machine shop products	3,847	72,572	90.09
Furniture	1,058	47,209	66.63
Hosiery and knit goods	448	49,770	62.81
Ironwork	639	26,810	56.43
Jewelry	666	27,225	61.26
Leather	386	88,682	58.75
Liquors, malt	728	281,615	127.32
Lumber	1,434	51,305	60.96
Printing, publishing, book and job	3,491	18,348	71.14′
Saddlery and harnesses	2,659	7,751	61.71
Silk and silk goods	362	86,191	54.88
Slaughtering and meat packing, wholesale	488	178,936	22.64
Soap and candles	423	55,366	57.19
Tobacco, chewing, smoking and snuff	175	117,128	42.89
Tobacco, cigars and cigarettes	7,464	6,123	46.89
Woolen goods	220	175,227	88.49

TABLE 7.4   Number of Establishments, Average Capital per
            Establishment, and Average Capital Required to Produce a
            Product Valued at $ 100 in the 165 Principal Cities and the
            United States Exclusive of These Cities for 25 Selected
            Industries, 1890 (Cont)

| | United States Exclusive of 165 Principal Cities | | |
Industry	Number of Establishments	Average Capital per Establishment	Average Amount of Capital Required for a Product Valued at $ 100
Agricultural implements	715	86,049	166.26
Boots and shoes	813	52,096	44.94
Brass cuttings and brass finishing	45	56,660	69.93
Chemicals	207	78,460	132.08
Clothing, men's	238	17,256	49.90
Clothing, women's	25	11,994	26.76
Cotton goods	530	317,324	136.49
Dyeing and finishing textiles	57	326,667	146.15
Flour and grist mill products	17,862	8,518	43.40
Foundry and machine shop products	2,628	37,963	101.24
Furniture	521	31,567	82.60
Hosiery and knit goods	348	81,352	89.19
Ironwork	85	56,899	65.50
Jewelry	117	35,166	79.66
Leather	1,210	38,868	58.78
Liquors, malt	520	52,799	126.51
Lumber	2,236	20,886	74.14
Printing and publishing, book and job	607	5,095	88.21
Saddlery and harnesses	5,272	2,795	75.29
Silk and silk goods	110	180,059	65.05
Slaughtering and meat packing wholesale	123	88,372	22.88
Soap and candles	155	9,041	52.84
Tobacco, chewing, smoking and snuff	220	47,018	57.28
Tobacco, cigars and cigarettes	3,492	3,956	42.88
Woolen goods	1,091	84,730	102.70

SOURCE: Eleventh Census of the United States, *Report on Manufacturing Industries: 1890*, Part II, *Statistics of Cities* (Washington, DC: U.S. Government Printing
Office, 1895): XVII.

Because of their timidity and reluctance to adopt new methods of capital accumulation, the growth rates in the mercantile cities slowed considerably. The underlying cause of their lackluster performance is not difficult to identify: in very few cases was there a significant injection of new industries into the old economic base. Those manufacturing industries that had been present during the mercantile stage of accumulation maintained their dominance throughout the industrial era. Since these manufacturing industries were not growing very rapidly, they provided little thrust to the local economy.

The failure of mercantile cities to capture many of the fastest-growing manufacturing industries may be seen by comparing Table 7.5 and Table 7.6. For every city, Table 7.5 lists the six largest manufacturing industries for 1880, ranked by gross value of product. In Table 7.6, the ten largest industries in terms of 1929 employment are listed for the same cities. In almost every case, the six major industries in the 1880 profile also dominate in 1929. Very little spinoff has occurred, and more importantly, very few new industries have been added. As of 1929, the only new addition in all six cities is "electrical machinery, apparatus and supplies."

Not only had these cities failed to update their manufacturing base, but even more significantly, most of the industries that were prominent in the mercantile cities had been generating below-average employment growth. Of the twenty-four industries included in Table 7.7, only eight registered above-average employment gains, and of those eight, only three—bread and bakery products, foundry and machine shop products, and electrical machinery—were present in most mercantile cities.

Industrial Cities and Industrial Accumulation.

If inertia was the primary barrier preventing old cities from pursuing industrial accumulation, then it is fair to ask why this same phenomenon did not affect the economic base in those cities that are now identified with the Industrial Revolution. In general, it would appear that two major factors stimulated the entrepreneurs in these cities to adopt different behavior pat-

TABLE 7.5   The Six Leading Industries Ranked by Gross Value of
Product in Six Mercentile Centers, 1880

New York	Philadelphia	Boston
1. Clothing, men's	1. Sugar and molasses	1. Sugar and molasses
2. Slaughtering	2. Woolen goods	2. Clothing, men's
3. Printing and publishing	3. Clothing, men's	3. Slaughtering
4. Malt liquors	4. Mixed textiles	4. Foundry and machine
5. Clothing, women's	5. Cotton goods	shop products
6. Tobacco, cigars, and	6. Carpets	5. Printing
cigarettes		6. Malt liquors

Baltimore	Cincinnati	St. Louis
1. Clothing, men's	1. Clothing, men's	1. Flour and grist mill
2. Fruits and vegetables	2. Slaughtering	products
3. Fertilizers	3. Foundry and	2. Slaughtering
4. Foundry and machine	machine shop	3. Foundry and machine
shop products	products	shop products
5. Boots and shoes	4. Distilled liquors	4. Tobacco, chewing
6. Tinware	5. Carriages and	5. Malt liquors
	wagons	6. Sugar and molasses
	6. Malt liquors	

SOURCE: Tenth Census of the United States, *Report Upon the Statistics of Manufacturers*, Vol 2 (Washington, DC: U.S. Government Printing Office, 1882): 26.

terns from those followed by their counterparts in the mercantile cities.

First, those cities that were later to emerge as major industrial centers generally began their economic life as mercantile outposts controlling relatively small hinterlands. They served primarily as transshipment centers or break-in-bulk points for goods that either originated in the major mercantile centers or were ultimately destined for these cities. As such, they were subordinate cogs within the mercantile system. Their fate depended solely on the establishment of viable commercial links with one of the seaport cities, and, as a result, their prosperity and destiny were intimately related to decisions that were beyond their control. Their autonomy as mercantile centers, in other words, was severely constrained. However, with the emergence of a national market generated by the canal and rail networks, an opportunity arose for these entrepreneurs to liberate themselves from mercantile-imposed development barriers.

TABLE 7.6   Ten Largest Industries As Measured by Number of Wage
Earners for Six Leading Mercentile Centers, 1929

New York	*Philadelphia*
Clothing, women's, n.e.c. (96,011)[a]	Knit goods (25,044)
Clothing n.e.c. (28,498)	Electrical machinery (16,492)
Printing and publishing, book and job (25,431)	Clothing n.e.c. (10,743)
Bread and other bakery products (23,383)	Foundry and machine shop products n.e.c. (10,101)
Boots and shoes (14,619)	Clothing, women (8,526)
Foundry and machine shop products n.e.c. (14,277)	Cigars and cigarettes (8,142)
Printing and publishing, newspaper and periodicals (13,026)	Worsted goods (7,734)
Electrical machinery, apparatus and supplies (12,740)	Bread and bakery products (7,401)
Knit goods (10,874)	Printing and publishing, newspapers and periodicals (6,913)
Furniture (10,738)	Printing and publishing, book and job (5,752)
Total manufacturing wage earners (563,249)	Total manufacturing wage earners (246,908)
Total in top 10 industries (249,597)	Total in top 10 industries (106,848)
Percentage of total in top 10 industries = 44.3	Percentage of total in top 10 industries = 43.2

Boston	*St. Louis*
Boots and shoes (6,817)	Foundry and machine shop products n.e.c. (5,059)
Clothing, women's n.e.c. (4,723)	Clothing, women's, n.e.c. (4,823)
Clothing, n.e.c. (3,941)	Clothing, n.e.c. (3,946)
Confectionary (3,970)	Bread and bakery products (3,881)
Printing and publishing, book and job (3,728)	Printing and publishing, book and job (3,463)
Printing and publishing, newspaper and periodicals (2,994)	Meat packing, wholesale (3,158)
Electrical machinery, apparatus and supplies (2,824)	Boxes, paper, n.e.c. (2,452)
Bread and bakery products (2,733)	Furniture (2,350)
Furniture (2,109)	Car and general construction and repairs, steam railroad repair shops (2,374)
Patent or proprietary medicines and compounds (1,048)	Cars, electric and steam railroad, not built in railroad repair shops (2,402)
Total manufacturing wage earners (75,907)	Stoves and ranges (other than electric) and warm air furnaces (1,834)
Total in top 10 industries (34,887)	Total manufacturing wage earners (109,010)
Percentage of total in top 10 industries = 45.9	Total in top 10 industries (35,792)
	Percentage of total in top 10 industries = 32.8

TABLE 7.6   Ten Largest Industries As Measured by Number of Wage
Earners for Six Leading Mercentile Centers, 1929 (Cont)

Baltimore	*Cincinnati*
Clothing n.e.c. (9,363)	Clothing n.e.c. (5,878)
Foundry and machine shop products, n.e.c. (4,002)	Foundry and machine shop products, n.e.c. (4,284)
Clothing, women's, n.e.c. (3,481)	Boots and shoes (2,951)
Furnishing goods, men's, n.e.c. (3,711)	Printing and publishing, book and job (2,861)
Bread and bakery products (2,885)	Bread and bakery products (2,332)
Tin cans and other tinware (4,392)	Meat packing, wholesale (1,644)
Fertilizers (2,596)	Printing and publshing, newspaper and periodicals (1,609)
Printing and publishing, book and job (2,400)	Stoves and ranges (other than electric) and warm air furnaces (989)
Ship and boat building, steel and wooden, including repair work (2,090)	Cooper, tin and sheet iron work, including galvanized-iron work, n.e.c. (911)
Nonferrous-metal alloys and products, not including aluminum products (1,872)	Confectionary (923)
Total manufacturing wage earners (85,655)	Total manufacturing ware earners (63,986)
Total in top 10 industries (36,792)	Total in top 10 industries (24,882)
Percentage of total in top 10 industries = 42.9	Percentage of total in top 10 industries = 38.3

SOURCE: Fifteenth Census of the United States, *Manufacturers: 1929*, Volume 3,
Report by States (Washington DC: U.S. Government Printing Office, 1933).
a.   Numbers in parentheses denote total employment in that industry in 1929.

If they could establish an independent economic base, then
unfettered prosperity was a definite possibility.

In addition, many entrepreneurs who would have sought to
emulate the eastern merchants realized that they had already
lost the battle for the initial advantage. By trying to compete as
mercantile centers, their cities would face the onerous task of
catching up with those cities blessed with the advantage of an
early start. However, manufacturing activities, especially in
those lines that had not been captured by the old cities during
the mercantile era, presented an opportunity to ascend the
urban hierarchy without competing directly with old cities.
Thus, because of both their subordinate position within the
mercantile system and the disadvantages associated with a late
start, the entrepreneurs in these cities were less wedded to the
old mode of capital accumulation. By breaking with past tradi-

TABLE 7.7   National Growth in Average Number of Wage Earners For
Selected Industries, 1899-1923

Industry	Growth in Wage Earners (percentages)
All industries	88.2
Slaughtering and meat packing	94.2
Bread and other bakery products	172.4
Clothing, women's	59.6
Clothing, men's	61.7
Knit goods	132.2
Carpets and rugs	24.0
Foundry and machine shop products	99.8
Stoves and hot air furnaces	9.5
Boots and shoes	58.8
Printing and publishing, newspapers and periodicals	27.8
Printing and publishing, book and job	7.1
Boxes, paper and other, n.e.c.	1.9
Druggists' preparations, patent medicines and compounds	78.9
Fertilizers	60.6
Copper, tin and sheet iron work	4.4
Tinware, n.e.c.	43.3
Tobacco, cigars, and cigarettes	27.7
Furniture	90.4
Steam railroad repair shops	181.6
Cars, steam railroad	129.0
Shipbuilding, steel	68.1
Electrical machinery, apparatus, and supplies	459.1
Confectionary	−9.7
Shipbuilding, wooden	−34.5

SOURCE: Bureau of the Census, *The Growth of Manufactures 1899 to 1923,*
Census Monographs VIII (Washington, DC: U.S. Government Printing Office, 1928):
Table 32.

tions, they could liberate their local economies and initiate a
new round of uneven development.

That some cities were able to navigate this uncharted course
toward prosperity is beyond doubt. Table 7.8 lists the rate of
population growth between 1870 and 1930 for seven mercantile
cities and thirteen industrial cities. In every case, the industrial
cities grew faster than their mercantile counterparts. However,
the decennial rate of growth for these industrial cities was quite
uneven. Some stopped growing relatively early in the industrial
era while others maintained their rapid pace through 1930.

TABLE 7.8   Population Growth Rates in Twenty Selected Cities,
1870-1930

	Decades					
City	1870-1880	1880-1890	1890-1900	1900-1910	1910-1920	1920-1930
New York[a]	32.4	41.4	37.0	38.6	15.1	23.3
Philadelphia	19.2	25.7	23.6	23.6	19.7	17.7
Boston	40.9	44.8	23.6	25.1	19.6	11.6
Baltimore	25.9	24.3	30.7	17.2	9.7	31.4
Cincinnati	18.0	16.4	9.8	11.6	10.4	12.4
St. Louis	12.8	28.9	27.3	19.4	12.5	6.3
Pittsburgh	78.7	68.8	46.3	31.3	18.2	10.2
Cleveland	72.5	63.2	46.1	46.9	42.1	13.0
Youngstown	91.1	115.2	35.1	76.2	67.4	28.4
Chicago	68.3	118.6	54.4	28.7	23.6	25.0
Milwaukee	61.8	76.9	39.5	31.0	22.3	26.5
Toledo	58.7	62.4	61.9	27.8	44.3	19.6
Dayton	26.9	58.3	39.4	36.6	30.9	31.7
Buffalo	31.8	64.8	37.8	20.2	19.6	13.1
Minneapolis	258.8	251.4	23.1	48.7	26.3	22.0
St. Paul	107.1	221.1	22.5	31.7	9.3	15.7
Birmingham	–	748.3	46.7	245.4	34.8	45.2
Rochester	43.2	49.8	21.4	34.2	35.6	10.9
Detroit	46.2	77.0	38.8	63.0	113.3	57.9
Akron	65.0	67.2	54.8	61.6	201.8	22.4

a. Figures for New York City represent the combined population growth rates of
New York and Brooklyn, which before 1898 were separate cities.

Both the timing and duration of these growth spurts can be
attributed directly to the type of industries found in each city.

In several instances, the growth of an industrial city was
linked to one specific industry. Automobiles in Detroit, tires in
Akron, and photographic equipment in Rochester all developed
after 1900. Consequently, the dynamic growth period in these
cities continued to either 1920 or 1930. In Pittsburgh, Cleveland, Youngstown, Buffalo, and Birmingham, the timing of the
growth spurt coincides with the dispersion of steel mills. However, in order to obtain a more comprehensive vision of the
relationship between urban growth and industrial accumulation,
we must consider the entire array of industries located in the
major industrial cities. Table 7.9 lists the ten leading industries
ranked according to 1929 employment for ten industrial cities.

The difference between their industrial profile and the 1929 industrial profile of the six mercantile cities is quite striking. While there are several instances of overlap—especially in the residentiary industries such as "bread and other bakery products," "printing and publishing," and "meat packing"—the industrial cities generally exhibit quite distinctive industrial profiles. The most prominent sectors are those associated with the iron and steel, automobile, and metalworking industries. None of these industries ever appeared in the 1929 industrial profile of any mercantile city.

The "newness" of these industries is apparent from their rapid growth. For example, employment in automobile bodies and parts rose from 1,810 in 1904 to 163,530 by 1923. From 1899 to 1923, automobile employment increased by *10,667.6%*. Other dynamic industries during this 24-year period are electrical machinery, apparatus, and supplies (459.1%); iron and steel, steel works, and rolling mills (111.9%); iron and steel, bolts, nuts, washers, and rivets (1C8.6%); optical goods (229.3%); and rubber tires and inner tubes (406.9%).[25] Thus, between 1880 and 1930, the industrial structure of the most rapidly growing cities contained industries whose rate of employment growth greatly exceeded the national rate of manufacturing employment growth. These were the new dynamic activities generated by the Industrial Revolution, and those cities that captured a significant share of these industries grew commensurately. The older mercantile cities, however, did not generate much employment in these new industries, and as a result, their growth was significantly below that of the industrial cities.

In conclusion, by breaking with past traditions, the emerging industrial cities could liberate their local economies from the shackles imposed by the mercantile system and initiate a new round of urban development based upon a new mode of capital accumulation. The mercantile cities, on the other hand, constrained by inertial forces that prevented a decisive shift to industrial accumulation, could not maintain their previous momentum. While they failed to surmount the barriers imposed by the waning efficacy of the mercantile system, the industrial

TABLE 7.9   The Ten Leading Industries Measured by Total Employment
For a Selected Group of Industrial Cities, 1929

Buffalo

Motor vehicles (6,060)
Foundry and machine shop products
   n.e.c. (5,841)
Car and general construction and
   repairs, steam railroad repair shops
   (3,447)
Iron and steel, steel works, and rolling
   mills (2,965)
Bread and bakery products (2,561)
Aircraft and parts (2,031)
Meat packing, wholesale (1,598)
Clothing n.e.c. (1,842)
Stamped ware and metal stamping
   (1,488)
Boxes, paper n.e.c. (1,280)
Total in top ten industries = 29,113
Total manufacturing wage earners
   (68,854)
Percentage of total in top 10 industries
   = 42.2

Cleveland

Foundry and machine shop products
   (16,730)
Motor vehicle bodies and motor vehicle
   parts (12,572)
Electrical machinery, apparatus, and
   supplies (6,454)
Clothing n.e.c. (5,645)
Bolts, nuts, washers, and rivets (5,031)
Clothing, women's, n.e.c. (3,759)
Machine tools (3,696)
Bread and bakery products (3,464)
Screw machine products (3,520)
Knit goods (2,760)
Total in top 10 industries = 63,631
Total manufacturing wage earners
   (146,881)
Percentage of total in top 10 industries
   = 43.3

Rochester

Clothing n.e.c. (10,647)
Electrical machinery, apparatus, and
   supplies (5,180)
Boots and shoes (4,390)
Optical goods (3,918)
Foundry and machine shop products
   n.e.c. (3,289)
Furniture (1,723)
Machine tools (1,671)
Boxes n.e.c. (1,186)
Bread and bakery products (1,033)
Lithographing (746)
Total in top 10 industries = 33,783
Total manufacturing wage earners
   (58,448)
Percentage of total in top 10 industries
   = 57.8

Dayton

The census indicates that no separate
industry figures are reported for
Dayton because to do so would disclose
specific firm data for the most
important industry, "Refrigerators,
mechanical."

Toledo

The census indicates that no separate
industry figures are reported for Toledo
because to do so would disclose specific
firm data for the most important
industry, "Motor vehicles."

TABLE 7.9   The Ten Leading Industries Measured by Total Employment
For a Selected Group of Industrial Cities, 1929 (Cont)

Akron

The census indiates that no separate industry figures are reported for Akron because to do so would disclose specific firm data for the most important industry, "Rubber tires and inner tubes."

Youngstown

The census indicates that no separate industry figures are reported for Youngstown because to do so would disclose specific firm data for the most important industry, "Iron and Steel: Steel Works and Rolling Mills."

Detroit

Motor vehicle bodies and parts (61,899)
Motor vehicles (50,082)
Foundry and machine shop products n.e.c. (9,095)
Machine tool accessories (7,880)
Bread and bakery products (5,151)
Printing and publishing, book and job (3,602)
Cigars and cigarettes (3,323)
Electrical and machinery, apparatus, and supplies (2,043)
Meat packing, wholesale (2,004)
Printing and publishing, newspaper, and periodicals (1,627)
Total in 10 top industries = 146,706
Total manufacturing wage earners (221,588)
Percentage of total in 10 top industries = 66.2

Chicago

Meatpacking, wholesale (25,491)
Furnishing goods, men's, n.e.c. (24,845)
Printing and publishing, book and job (24,043)
Clothing, men's, n.e.c. (17,706)
Furniture (15,084)
Iron and steel, steel works, and rolling mills (14,306)
Cars and general construction and steam railroad repair shops (12,662)
Bread and bakery products (12,359)
Clothing, women's, n.e.c. (11,590)
Confectionary (10,523)
Total in top 10 industries = 168,609
Total manufacturing wage earners (405,399)
Percentage of total in top 10 industries = 41.5

Pittsburgh

Iron and steel, steel works and rolling mills (10,644)
Bread and bakery products (5,135)
Foundry and machine shop products n.e.c. (4,689)
Bolts, nuts, washers, and rivets (2,380)
Confectionary (1,656)
Printing and publishing, book and job (1,654)

TABLE 7.9   The Ten Leading Industries Measured by Total Employment
For a Selected Group of Industrial Cities, 1929 (Cont)

Pittsburg (Cont)

Printing and publishing, newspaper and
   periodicals (1,459)
Meatpacking, wholesale (1,397)
Structural and ornamental iron and
   steel work (830)
Clothing, men's, n.e.c. (533)
Total in top 10 industries = 30,377
Total manufacturing wage earners
   (61,503)
Percentage of total in top 10 industries
   = 49.3

cities perceived the declining prominence of mercantile accumulation and used the opportunity to emerge from their dependent subordinate status. As a result, the role of leader and laggard was reversed, and the urban system experienced a second round of uneven, divergent development.

The South and Industrial Accumulation

The South, however, was not as fortunate as the industrial Midwest. Although the South, too, was in a subordinate position during the mercantile era, the emergence of industrial methods of capital accumulation did little to ameliorate its inferior position. In fact, as this second developmental phase progressed, the South's relative and absolute deprivation increased. Not only were mercantile methods siphoning any investable surplus from this region, but now industrial practices were also employed to preclude self-sustained growth. The predicament of the South is vividly captured by the following quote from Henry Grady, the editor of the *Atlantic Constitution:*

He gets up at the alarm of a Connecticut clock. Puts his Chicago suspenders on a pair of Detroit overalls. Washes his face with Cincinnati soap in a Philadelphia washpan. Works all day on a farm fenced with Pittsburgh wire and covered by an Ohio Mortgage. Comes home at night and reads a Bible printed in Chicago and says a prayer written in Jerusalem. And when he dies . . . the South doesn't furnish a thing meant for his funeral but the corpse and the hole in the ground.[26]

Although Reconstruction certainly contributed to the South's dependent status, many other structural conditions also served as barriers blocking its development. Among the more significant were the post-Civil War agricultural system, absentee ownership of industrial facilities, and various freight rate arrangements.

That the South was laboring under all the disadvantages associated with a one-crop economy was recognized well before the Civil War. For example, in 1826 it was noted that

> There is not a finer grazing country in the world than South Carolina; and, were attention paid to the raising of cattle, sheep, goats, hogs, horses, mules, etc., this state might supply itself as well as all the West India Islands with these useful animals; but every other object gives place to cotton. Immense numbers of cattle, hogs, horses and mules are driven annually from the western country into this state, and sold to advantage.[27]

After the Civil War, the situation failed to improve. In South Carolina, for example, agricultural dependency on "foreign" products increased while cotton production exploded. Between 1860 and 1880, the hay crop declined from 87,000 tons to 2,700 tons while cotton production increased from 353,000 bales to 522,000.[28] In large part, the root of the problem can be traced to the fact that "at least half the planters after 1870 were either northern men or were supported by northern money." The link between northern money and southern agriculture was the lien system used to provide agricultural credit.[29] Under this system southern farmers who needed credit would pledge their unplanted crop as collateral to a merchant who advanced the needed supplies. Once the lien was executed, the farmer was prohibited from purchasing on credit supplies from any other source and, in addition, could only sell the crop to his creditor. Since the merchant set the crop and supply price, the farmer was forced to buy dear and sell cheap. After interest charges were also included, it was a rare occurrence for a farmer to "pay out" his debt in one season. Hence, he was forced to enter into a similar arrangement with the same creditor in the following year and as a result, he "usually passed into a state of helpless peonage." With no recourse to other sources of credit, the farmer was forced to plant cotton—the one cash crop that the merchants would accept in exchange for credit—despite the fact that it was depleting the soil and glutting the market. Hence, these practices blocked the development of a more balanced agricultural system. Although northern merchants profited from this arrangement, southerners sunk deeper into rural poverty.

While effective control of southern agriculture had passed to northern finance interests despite nominal southern ownership, northern control of southern industrial facilities was almost absolute. According to Woodward, "The Morgans, Mellons, and Rockefellers sent their agents to take charge of the region's railroads, mines, furnaces, and financial corporations, and eventually many of its distributive institutions. . . . The economy over which they presided was increasingly coming to be one of branch plants, branch banks, captive mines and chain stores."[30] The effect was so pernicious that in 1946 one northern journalist characterized Texas as "New York's most valuable foreign possession."[31]

The National Emergence Council lent credence to this description when it reported:

Lacking capital of its own, the South has been forced to borrow from outside financiers, who have reaped a rich harvest in the form of interest and dividends. At the same time it has had to hand over the control of much of its business and industry to investors from wealthier sections. . . . This has turned policy making powers over to outside managements whose other interests often lead them to exercise their authority against the South's best advantage. For example, many such companies buy most of their goods outside the South, and often their sales policies are dictated in the interests of allied corporations in other sections of the country.[32]

The Birmingham steel industry presents a striking example of northern ownership throttling southern industrial development. In 1898, Birmingham was the world's third largest producer of pig iron, and in 1893, the South accounted for 22% of the nation's pig iron production. But between 1903 and 1913, pig iron production in the South remained stationary while it expanded by 70% nationally.[33] The failure of southern production to expand is even more startling since most authorities concede that Birmingham mills had the lowest cost in the nation. Two related factors account for the moribund condition of the southern steel industry. First, most southern steel capacity was acquired by the Morgan empire when it amalgamated the Tennessee Iron and Coal Company with U.S. Steel. Then they instituted the Pittsburgh Plus pricing system for the express purpose of concentrating steel production in the less efficient northeastern areas.

Many other southern manufacturing activities saw their markets constricted by the prevailing freight rate system which discriminated against southern producers.[34] Although most evidence demonstrates that there were no cost differentials between southern and northern railroads, southern producers were required by the ICC to pay higher freight charges for shipping their products a given distance than were their northern competitors. As a result, this barrier protected northern producers from southern competition. For example, under this system, it was often more expensive to ship southern products 400 miles from the South into the northern consuming area than it was for a northern manufacturer to ship his goods 700 miles solely within the Northeast. As a result, southern producers were excluded from the lucrative consumer markets in the Northeast, while the asymmetrical nature of the freight rate system did not limit northern producers from invading southern markets.

RISE OF THE SUNBELT CITIES

The previous two historical vignettes analyzed the motivations of the major economic actors during each era and assessed the impact of their decisions on urban growth. We saw that the mercantile cities rose to metropolitan status as a result of the desire of a group of merchants to create the infrastructure required for an exchange economy. Through their actions and policies the last vestiges of a self-sufficient economy were destroyed and replaced by a national market economy. Actions in the sphere of exchange dominated the economy during this period and those cities controlling this development became the leading mercantile centers in the United States. However, when these same economic actors were unable to redirect their actions, the local economies which they controlled stagnated relative to those in a new set of cities.

In the second wave of urbanization, the arena shifted to the sphere of production. Those entrepreneurs in the subordinate tier of mercantile cities who recognized the potential inherent in industrial production guided their cities into the upper echelons of the urban system. In a sense, their failure to achieve an initial advantage in mercantile pursuits proved to be a blessing in disguise. Faced with a dependent secondary status and relatively free from the inertial forces generated by the old and by now outmoded form of capital accumulation, these individuals had relatively little to lose by venturing into a new realm of capital accumulation. While the mercantile cities had failed to develop a new set of dynamic manufacturing activities, the subordinate cities became the location for the new manufacturing city-building activities.

This brings us to the third wave of urban development, euphemistically called the "rise of the Sunbelt." Traditional location and regional development theory suggests that the economic development of this region is a natural outcome of free market processes. Cheap land for space-extensive manufacturing activities, low wage rates, low taxes, and a docile labor force all combine to make this region the most logical and cost efficient location for both new dynamic activities and old slowly growing industries. While there is no denying the accuracy of these statements, they are incomplete explanations that fail to address both the internal economic dynamics and the motivations of the dominant economic actors.

In many superficial respects, this third era resembles the history of the previous two epochs. A set of barriers arose and prevented a continuation of the old industrial methods of capital accumulation. These barriers created opportunities for those entrepreneurs who could successfully catapult the economy onto a new growth trajectory. As the fate of various regions hung precariously in the balance, a struggle ensued over which region and set of cities would seize the opportunity. Would the northeastern metropolitan areas overcome the internal contradictions generated by the passing of the industrial era or would the mantle of growth shift to a new set of cities? If the former scenario prevailed, then the economy would witness a further intensification of the old pattern of regional uneven development as growth in the industrial cities produced increased poverty and underdevelopment in the South. But if the Sunbelt cities could capture a significant portion of the new epoch-defining activities, then the role of leader and laggard would be reversed, and a new regional pattern of uneven development would emerge. All of these problems were not new. As the economy emerged from the stage of mercantile accumulation, the same constellation of issues, barriers, and opportunities was present, albeit in a slightly modified form.

But upon closer examination, the rise of the Sunbelt highlights several factors that were absent in previous epochs and these additional features account for the contentious debate that has embroiled the Sunbelt in a "second war between the states." Had the Sunbelt simply captured a large proportion of the new epoch-defining activities, then the level of interregional dissension would have been less. However, in the present era, the rise of the Sunbelt represents a serious threat to the continued vitality and viability of the economic base of northeastern urban areas. In previous epochs, the appearance of new members in the system of cities was not considered to be the cause of death in the older cities. While local businessmen were distressed at the prospect of flagging growth, as long as the city could maintain its former economic base, absolute decline could be avoided. Therefore, uneven development was only a relative proposition. One set of cities would lose their prominent position as the most rapidly growing urban areas and descend in rank through the urban hierarchy—although they would still be growing with respect to population and jobs—while another group assumed the role of growth leader. However, as the current indices of population migration and job loss indicate, in the present wave of uneven urban development, absolute decline has replaced relative decline as the dominant motif. This, in turn, has raised the stakes for the growth laggards and heightened their sense of crisis.

Moreover, as if to add insult to injury, the rapid ascent of the Sunbelt represents a dramatic break with past conditions. Not only have the northeastern cities lost their position as the preeminent national urban centers, but their role at the top has been usurped by a region that has overcome the deeply embedded subordination created by two epochs of carefully constructed institutional and economic barriers. While the northeastern cities were burdened with an old, slowly growing industrial foundation, the Sunbelt cities were in a more flexible position to conform to the new economic requirements. In a sense, they presented the economy with a *tabula rasa*, uncluttered with the outmoded infrastructure and habits from previous eras. Thus, the tables have been turned. While the northeastern cities are losing population and jobs at an alarming rate, the Sunbelt is picking up the slack and leading the economy into new rounds of capital accumulation.

However, despite the population and job losses in the Northeast and the simultaneous growth in the Sunbelt, it would be a mistake to assume that the Sunbelt has risen by pirating economic activity from the older industrial centers. Clearly, the economic prowess of the Sunbelt cannot be attributed simply to its more hospitable location for transplanted northeastern industries. Otherwise, the Sunbelt would be nothing more than a relocated carbon copy of the industrial Northeast. Since this is not the case, we are left in a quandary: how can we explain the dual phenomenon of growth in the Sunbelt coupled with decay in the Northeast without resorting to the overly simplistic assumption that the Sunbelt cities are replicating the industrial structure of their older, northeastern counterparts?

The solution rests with the way industrial activity diffuses throughout the various regions of a country. Specifically, an unindustrialized area can expand its economic base by any combination of three devices—physical relocation, branch plants, or the adoption of new, leading-edge activities. Depending on the mix, the region will either remain mired in its subordinate, dependent status or it can break the barriers associated with the old mode of capital accumulation, initiate a new round of uneven development, and thereby reverse the roles of regional leader and laggard. Southerners tried all of these devices at various times but soon realized that two of them—physical relocation and branch plants—were seriously deficient methods for achieving self-sustained development.

Physical relocation entails the actual movement of a production facility from one location to another. The former site is abandoned, and a new location, blessed with a more favorable constellation of factor costs, is selected as a replacement. In the traditional parlance of urban economics, this is known as industrial spinoff. Thompson, for example, describes the metamorphosis of the New York industrial base in terms of its propensity for industrial spinoff. He writes, "The New York metropolitan area grew by incubating new functions, maturing them, and finally spinning them off to other sections of the country, all the while regenerating this cycle. . . . Currently, New York is losing the manufacturing end of its most traditional specialties as garment sewing slips away to low-wage Eastern Pennsylvania leaving only the selling function behind, and as printing split away from immobile publishing."[35]

However, several factors militate against lending too much credence to this process. Although physical relocation may produce adverse economic effects in the region or city that is losing economic activity, it is questionable whether the recipient region could reverse the process of uneven development solely by accepting those industries that have been cast off by the more developed areas. As Thompson's quote indicates, industries that are spun off are generally mature, low-wage activities. Their growth is relatively anemic, and unless the receiving region can absorb large quantities of these activities, its growth will stagnate. Moreover, the low wages would fail to generate sufficient income to support all the ancillary, nonbasic activities that are generally associated with a developed regional economy. Therefore, if a region only receives the mature, low-wage industries that are spun off from the more developed area, this indicates that the recipient has failed to overcome its colonial status.

Branch plants can produce a shift in the regional alignment of industries in several ways—all of which obviate the need for physical relocation. If a firm wishes to expand, it can either build an additional plant in the old region or it can decide to construct the new facility in a new region. Similarly, if it already has several plants scattered in various regions, then its decision as to which plant will receive additional capital infusions will also alter the preexisting regional balance of industrial activity. Finally, the firm can choose to abandon one of its branch plants while centralizing all activity in the remaining facilities. Irrespective of which situation actually prevails, the results will be the same; one region will grow while another either stagnates or declines. Thus, we can have uneven development in the absence of physical relocation.

However, in view of the traditional southern antipathy toward absentee ownership, it is unlikely that branch plants were a significant factor in the rapid ascent of the Sunbelt. While it is true that they are an excellent method for developing new industrial facilities in a region that is plagued by a shortage of indigenous capital, the dynamics of this process make it unlikely that branch plants could produce the high growth rates found in the Sunbelt. In the first place, profit repatriation would ensure that any investable surplus accruing to these facilities would leave the region. This, in turn, would prevent the initiation of a substantial self-sustained growth process and as a result, the region receiving the branch plants would find the pace of development controlled by "foreign" investors. In short, "this way depends upon the initiative and decisions of companies outside the region. There is little the region can do to speed up the process."[36] Thus, if a region is dependent upon branch plants as the dominant source of its industrial development, this too is a signal that the region has failed to alter its subordinate status. Branch plants are a barrier, not an opportunity for reversing the roles of leader and laggard.

This leaves one other strategy for an underdeveloped region to assume the role of growth leader. If new dynamic industries choose to locate in the underdeveloped region and bypass the old, industrialized areas, then a new round of divergent, uneven development can occur. According to Sale,[37] this process is primarily responsible for the rapid rise of the Sunbelt. In the postwar phase of capital accumulation, six new pillars of growth—agribusiness, defense, advanced technology, oil and natural gas production, real estate and construction, and tourism and leisure—have emerged as the dominant industries. All have chosen a Sunbelt location. Northeastern cities have failed to capitalize on the opportunities presented by these new industries. As a result, they have been mired in stagnation caused by their reliance on an outmoded, mature, and slow-growing industrial base. In short, when the end of the Industrial Revolution era placed barriers in the path of the old modes of capital accumulation, the northeastern cities were unable to rejuvenate themselves by capturing these new industries. The Sunbelt, on the other hand, was in the midst of a thorough reorganization and rationalization of its economic base. Thus, it was perfectly situated to profit from the barriers blocking further progress based upon the old, industrial technologies.

The Reorganization of the Southern Economy

Once the Industrial Revolution had run its course, the U.S. economy faced severe readjustment problems. The first signal that a change was in the offing was the trauma of the 1929 depression. However, although the outward manifestations of the problem first became painfully obvious in 1929, in retrospect, several economic historians place the first signs of trouble ten years earlier. Both Kuznets and Creamer demonstrate that beginning in 1919, the capital-output ratio began a slow secular decline.[38] They give two reasons to explain this trend. First, they argue that up to 1920, large investments in fixed capital and infrastucture were needed before production could commence. This raised the ratio of capital expenditures to output and was a major factor accounting for the buoyancy of the economy during the industrial epoch. Yet once the investment was complete, output could rise dramatically. As a result, the need for further increments of plant and equipment was reduced and the investment component of aggregate demand declined. Second, they argue that the rising burden of depreciation expenses induced businessmen to economize on the use of capital. This was accomplished by developing new capital efficient technologies which, in turn, produced an unintended falling level of investment.

As the economy descended into the depths of depression, it was obvious that the old business as usual attitudes could not correct the present malady. Unless new modes of capital accumulation could provide opportunities for the economy to break the barrier of insufficient aggregate demand, the prospects for further growth in the old industrial cities would remain bleak. Thus, according to both Kuznets and Creamer, the market was the primary barrier blocking continued economic development. Until aggregate demand could be raised to a more adequate level, the economy would continue to stagnate. However, the elimination of this barrier through the advent of Keynesian-inspired federal policies provided an opportunity for a new phase of capital accumulation and its concomitant new wave of urbanization. The region that benefited most from these demand-stimulating programs was the Sunbelt, while the biggest losers were the old mercantile and industrial cities in the Northeast.

However, this change did not occur overnight, and, indeed, many Southerners at first believed that Keynesian policies were simply another mechanism to maintain their subordinate status. As late as the end of the Korean War, Southerners were sure that their role would be limited to a reservoir of cheap labor. When northern labor markets were tight, Southerners would be encouraged to migrate and accept the available factory jobs.

When demand declined, they would lose their jobs and endure several more years of rural poverty. This belief was so pervasive that one congressional report argued that the South's principal crop was labor for northern factories and not cotton:

> In normal and boom years, that crop is "harvested" when the South "gives away" to the rest of the country some thousands of young men and women, principally between the ages of 25 and 35. . . . In depression years, the market for these "free goods" fails and the region is forced to carry the excess supply until demand revives. In a very real sense, the South has been acting as a reservoir of labor for the Nation as a whole. During the recent war, that reservoir of labor was of enormous importance in manning war plants from Massachusetts to California. For these reasons, the number of those migrants and the education and training they receive is a national, and not merely a regional problem.[39]

An Alabama tenant farmer echoed these sentiments when he remarked, "Yup, last year Charlie Wilson sent my boy home from Korea. This year he's going to send him home from Detroit."[40]

In addition to complaining about their role as the balance wheel for the national economy, many Southerners argued that migration to the North robbed the South of its most productive citizens, created a financial drain, and ensured continued regional poverty. For example, Coyle estimated that over a ten-year period, this migration cost the South $36 billion.[41] A later study declared that "Tennessee, in effect, has exported to other states a staggering $2,280 million investment in production manpower over the past eight years."[42] Vance summarized the southern view that high rates of outmigration would leave the South destitute when he wrote "the South is not competent under its present economy to rear and educate and send out the nation's population reserves. Not only is this region too poor, such a process means a constant drain on its resources."[43]

As a result of this migration, the South was caught in a vicious circle. In order to develop, it had to retain those young, educated people who were most inclined to leave. But these people would not remain in the South as long as the region was an underdeveloped, rural area offering no hope of advancement. To solve this problem, agriculture had to be reorganized and industry had to be attracted. Both tasks required federal assistance.

The main barrier blocking southern prosperity stemmed from that region's semicolonial agricultural system. A 1947 congressional report on the economic problems of the cotton belt, succinctly catalogued the problems in the agricultural sector:

> The economy of the South is basically agricultural. The region produces vast quantities of agricultural and other raw products, large quantities of which are shipped to other areas for processing and manufacture. In many ways the South has served as a colonial empire to other regions of the nation. Much of the wealth of the region has been owned or controlled by outside interests. Credit to an important extent has been either directly or indirectly in the hands of outsiders; the transportation system has been geared to encourage the outshipment of raw materials and discourage the shipment of finished products.[44]

Because of these conditions the report noted that the South was plagued by "low crop yields, inefficient livestock production, depleted soils, inadequate land and capital resources per family, poor farm organization, and a low level of managerial ability."[45]

On a more concrete level, the depressed condition of southern agriculture can be summarized by a few salient statistics. In 1940, one-third of all employed Southerners worked on farms and received less than one-sixth of the total regional income. In that same year the average value of machinery and equipment per southern farm was 75% less than the comparable figure for midwestern farms. In 1929, cotton contributed 46% of all cash receipts from southern farms. Seventeen years later, its dominant position had declined, but with the exception of tobacco, no other crop accounted for as much as 5% of total cash receipts.

The rural poverty in the South was staggering. In 1934, more than half of all southern farmers did not own their own land. In seven cotton states, the average annual net income for all sharecroppers was $312 per family, or $71 per person. In the Mississippi delta, one of the nation's most fertile agricultural regions, net farm income was only $38 per person and only 70% of all sharecropper families had any cash remaining after settling with their creditors. In North Carolina, the average value of tenant farmer homes was $417. In Alabama, the average home for black sharecroppers was valued at only $194.[46]

In view of this grinding poverty, it is not surprising that so many Southerners chose to abandon farming and search for alternative employment. However, for those who were reluctant to find another occupation, agricultural policies initiated during the New Deal and completed after World War II provided an additional push. In August 1933, the Agricultural Adjustment Administration adopted a price support program that included restrictions on the number of acres that each farmer could cultivate. In return for leaving a portion of their land fallow, each farmer would receive payments from the federal government. However, there were few controls to ensure an equitable division of benefit payments between the landlord and his tenant. In theory, those tenants who owned their own equipment and paid a cash rent would receive the full benefit while those tenants who paid a rent in kind would receive a prorated payment from their landlord. Farm laborers were entitled to nothing. In practice, the tenants rarely received any benefit payments and thus, acreage restrictions left them without an income. Moreover, landlords had a new incentive to consolidate their holdings and convert their tenants into hired laborers. This not only freed the landlords from any financial obligation to their employees, but it also encouraged farm mechanization and additional rural depopulation.

By itself, the shift of the southern labor force out of agriculture could not alleviate the region's underdeveloped status. Although individual Southerners may have benefited by leaving agriculture, the region as a whole faced a drain of human capital. Therefore, for the South to prosper, industrialization would have to accompany agricultural reorganization. At this point, federal policies to boost aggregate demand coincided with the developmental needs of the Sunbelt. For example, if the Sunbelt was to pose a serious competitive threat to the economic dominance of the Northeast, its woefully inadequate infrastructure would have to be improved. Without this essential ingredient, the latent attractiveness of the region could not be exploited. Therefore, if the South desired to attract new dynamic activities, its next task would have to be the construction of a more conducive infrastructure.

Under these circumstances, the needs of the Sunbelt meshed with the demand stimulating policies of the federal government. If northeastern central cities could no longer profitably absorb sufficient new investment, then federal spending priorities could be shifted to new areas. Creating these facilities in the Sunbelt and suburbs required massive public outlays for road construction and the expansion of ancillary support services such as electric, sewage, and water facilities. In addition, these expenditures created fertile areas for the private sector in the form of new opportunities to construct stores, shopping plazas, and office complexes. When coupled with the large multiplier effect generated by these projects, the lagging investment sector of the economy received a powerful stimulus while the Sunbelt received the necessary rejuvenation of its physical environment.

Moreover, the design of these projects provided an additional stimulus to aggregate demand. For example, the low-density settlement patterns fostered a dependency on the automobile and all but eliminated the possibility of installing more efficient and hence less demand-stimulating mass transportation systems. Also, low-density, single-family housing requires larger outlays for public services, construction materials, and operating costs.[47] All of the extra demand engendered by these settlement patterns helped to stimulate the economy and were at least implicitly sanctioned by various public expenditure and tax policies. To the extent that the uncluttered virgin territory in the Sunbelt was most amenable to these programs, the rise of the Sunbelt coincided with the requirements of the Keynesian phase of capital accumulation.

But even with the construction of an adequate built environment, the Sunbelt was not prepared to assume the role of growth leader. In a sense, these preliminary steps were necessary but not sufficient. The missing ingredient was the adoption of a new dynamic industrial base. However, this too was an offshoot of federal demand-stimulating programs in the form of the military industrial complex. Electronics, research and development facilities, calculators, semiconductors, aeronautics, scientific instruments, and space exploration—to name only a few of the most dynamic industries created by the partnership between big business and big government—are all located primarily in the Sunbelt. But without direct federal involvement in their inception and maturation, it is doubtful that their growth and economic significance would have been as dramatic.

Thus, in the third phase of capital accumulation, federal spending promoted both the construction of the necessary infrastructure and the development of new dynamic industries. As a result, both regions were profoundly influenced by the policies designed to surmount the barrier of insufficient aggregate demand. The Sunbelt prospered from all phases of federal intervention and assumed the mantle of growth leadership. The northeastern central cities, however, were not as fortunate, and thus they lost their position as growth leaders within the U.S. system of cities.

NOTES

1. For an analysis of early urban growth rates, see George Rogers Taylor, "American Urban Growth Preceding the Railway Age," *Journal of Economic History* 27, 3 (1967): 309-339.

2. Quoted in Guy S. Callender, "The Early Transportation and Banking Enterprises of the States in Relation to the Growth of Corporations," *Quarterly Journal of Economics* 17, 1 (1902): 123.

3. Allen R. Pred, *Urban Growth and the Circulation of Information* (Cambridge, MA: Harvard Univ. Press, 1972): 114.

4. George Rogers Taylor, *The Transportation Revolution* (New York: Holt, Rinehart & Winston, 1964): 133.

5. For an excellent summary of the early history of these inland mercantile centers, see Richard Wade, *The Urban Frontier* (Chicago: Univ. of Chicago Press, 1959).

6. For an example of some of the public financing methods devised by mercantile interests, see Carter Goodrich, "The Revulsion Against Internal Improvements," *Journal of Economic History* 10, 2 (1950): 145-169; and Carter Goodrich and Harvey Segal, "Baltimore's Aid to Railroads—A Survey in the Municipal Planning of Internal Improvements," *Journal of Economic History* 13, 1 (1953): 2-35.

7. Charles N. Glaab and Theodore Brown, *A History of Urban America* (New York: Macmillan, 1967): 44.

8. H. Jerome Cranmer, "Canal Investment, 1815-1860," in William Parker (ed.), *Trends in the American Economy in the Nineteenth Century* (Princeton, NJ: Princeton Univ. Press, 1960): 555-556.

9. John Bell Rae, "Federal Land Grants in Aid of Canals," *Journal of Economic History* 4, 2 (1944): 167-177.

10. Taylor, *The Transportation Revolution:* 49.

11. Callender, op. cit.: 114.

12. Quoted in Thomas C. Cochran and William Miller, *The Age of Enterprise* (New York: Harper & Row, 1961): 57.

13. Albert Fishlow, "Ante Bellum Interregional Trade Reconsidered," *American Economic Review* 54 (May 1964): 355.

14. For an analysis of early southern attempts to construct a system of internal improvements, see Milton S. Heath, "Public Railroad Construction and the Development of Private Enterprise in the South Before 1861," *Journal of Economic History* 10 (Supplement 1950): 40-53.

15. Thomas Prentice Kettell, *Southern Wealth and Northern Profits* (Montgomery: Univ. of Alabama Press, 1965). Also, see Philip Foner, *Business and Slavery: The New York Merchants and the Irrepressible Conflict* (Chapel Hill: Univ. of North Carolina Press, 1941).

16. Quoted in Robert G. Albion, *The Rise of the New York Port* (New York: Charles Scribner's Sons, 1939): 94.

17. Ibid.: 121.

18. Theodore Marburg, "Income Originating in Trade," in William Parker, op. cit.: 321.

19. Quoted by Ralph W. Hasking, "Planter and Cotton Factor in the Old South," in Alfred D. Chandler, Stuart Bruchey, and Louis Golambos (eds.), *The Changing Economic Order* (New York: Harcourt Brace Jovanovich, 1968): 98.

20. Tenth Census of the United States, *Report Upon the Statistics of Manufacturers*, Volume II (Washington, DC: U.S. Government Printing Office, 1883): XXII.

21. Edward Kirkland, *Industry Comes of Age* (Chicago: Holt, Rinehart & Winston, 1961): 163.

22. Allen R. Pred, *The Spatial Dynamics of U.S. Urban Industrial Growth, 1800-1914* (Cambridge, MA: MIT Press, 1966): 18.

23. Robert M. Fogelson, *The Fragmented Metropolis* (Cambridge, MA: Harvard Univ. Press, 1967): 125.

24. Paul Mantoux, *The Industrial Revolution in the Eighteenth Century* (New York: Harper & Row, 1961): 368-369.

25. These growth rates are derived from Bureau of the Census, *The Growth of Manufacturers, 1899-1923*, Census Monographs VIII (Washington, DC: U.S. Government Printing Office, 1928): Table 32.

26. Quoted in Joseph Persky, "The South: A Colony at Home," *Southern Exposure* 1, 2 (1973): 16.

27. Quoted in Callender, op. cit.: 127.

28. C. Vann Woodward, *The Origins of the New South, 1877-1913* (Baton Rouge: Louisiana State Univ. Press, 1951): 178.

29. For an explanation of the crop lien system and its detrimental effects on southern agriculture, see Woodward, op. cit.: Chapter 7; Thomas D. Clark, "The Furnishing and Supply System in Southern Agriculture Since 1865," Journal of *Southern History* 12, 1 (1946): 24-44; Thomas D. Clark, "Imperfect Competition in the Southern Retail Trade After 1865," *Journal of Economic History* 3, Supplement (1948): 38-47; and George L. Anderson, "The South and the Problems of Post-Civil War Finance," *Journal of Southern History* 9, 2 (1943): 181-185.

30. Woodward, op. cit.: 292.

31. Quoted in Clarence Danhoff, "Four Decades of Thought on the South's Economic Problems," in Melvin L. Greenhut and W. Tate Whitman (eds.), *Essays in Southern Economic Development* (Chapel Hill: Univ. of North Carolina Press, 1964): 42.

32. National Emergency Council, *Report on Economic Conditions of the South* (Washington, DC: U.S. Government Printing Office, 1938): 53-54. Also, see Wendell Berge, "Monopoly and the South," *Southern Economic Journal* 13, 4 (1947): 360-369.

33. Woodward, op. cit.: 299-302.

34. For a description of freight rate discrimination and its detrimental impact on southern industrial development, see David M. Potter, "The Historical Development of Eastern-Southern Freight Rate Relationships," *Law and Contemporary Problems* 12, 3 (1947): 416-448; Frank L. Barton, "The Freight Rate Structure and the Distribution of Defense Contracts," *Southern Economic Journal* 8, 2 (1942): 122-133; and Milton S. Heath, "The Uniform Class Rate Decision and Its Implications for Southern Economic Development," *Southern Economic Journal* 12, 3 (1946): 213-237.

35. Wilbur Thompson, *A Preface to Urban Economics* (Baltimore: Johns Hopkins Univ. Press, 1965): 37.

36. Calvin B. Hoover, *Economy of the South*, Report of the Joint Committee On the Economic Report on the Impact of Federal Policies on the Economy of the South, 81st Cong., 1st Sess., 1949: 27.

37. Kirkpatrick Sale, *Power Shift* (New York: Random House, 1976): Chapter 1.

38. Simon Kuznets, *Capital in the American Economy* (Princeton, NJ: Princeton Univ. Press, 1961); and Daniel Creamer, Sergei P. Dobrovolsky, and Israel Borenstein, *Capital in Manufacturing and Mining* (Princeton, NJ: Princeton Univ. Press, 1960).

39. Hoover, op. cit.: 6-7.

40. Quoted in Vernon W. Ruttan, "Industrial Progress and Rural Stagnation in the New South," *Social Forces* 34, 2 (1955): 114-117.

41. David C. Coyle, "The South's Unbalanced Budget," *Virginia Quarterly Review* 13, 2 (1937): 207.

42. Quoted in Danhoff, op. cit.: 17.

43. Rupert B. Vance, *All These People* (Chapel Hill: Univ. of North Carolina Press, 1945): 278.

44. U.S. Congress, *Study of the Agricultural and Economic Problems of the Cotton Belt,* Hearings before the Special Subcommittee on Cotton of the Committee on Agriculture, 80th Cong., 1st Sess., July 7-8, 1947: 59.

45. Ibid.: 18.

46. Broadus Mitchel, *The Industrial Revolution in the South* (Baltimore: Johns Hopkins Univ. Press, 1930): 211-212.

47. Council on Environmental Quality, *Fifth Annual Report* (Washington, DC: U.S. Government Printing Office, 1974): 9-12.

BIBLIOGRAPHY

BOOKS

ALBION, R. (1937) The Rise of the New York Port. New York: Charles Scribner's Sons.

ALEXANDERSSON, G. (1956) The Industrial Structure of American Cities. Lincoln: Univ. of Nebraska Press.

ALONSO, W. (1964) Location and Land Use. Cambridge, MA: Harvard Univ. Press.

BELCHER, W. (1947) The Economic Rivalry Between St. Louis and Chicago. New York: Columbia Univ. Press.

BELL, D. (1973) The Coming of Post-Industrial Society. New York: Basic Books.

BERRY, B. [ed.] (1972) City Classification Handbook. New York: John Wiley.

––– (1967) Geography of Market Centers and Retail Distribution. Englewood Cliffs, NJ: Prentice-Hall.

––– and A. PRED (1965) Central Place Studies: A Bibliography of Theory and Applications. Philadelphia: Regional Science Research Institute.

BOGUE, D. (1971) The Structure of the Metropolitan Community. New York: Russel & Russel.

BORTS, G. and J. STEIN (1964) Economic Growth in a Free Market. New York: Columbia Univ. Press.

BURNS, A. F. (1934) Production Trends in the United States Since 1870. New York: National Bureau of Economic Research.

CARO, R. (1975) The Power Broker. New York: Random House.

CHAMBERLIN, E. (1946) The Theory of Monopolistic Competition. Cambridge, MA: Harvard Univ. Press.

CHINITZ, B. (1960) Freight and the Metropolis. Cambridge, MA: Harvard Univ. Press.

CHRISTALLER, W. (1966) The Central Places of Southern Germany. Englewood Cliffs, NJ: Prentice-Hall.

COCHRAN, T. and W. MILLER (1961) The Age of Enterprise. New York: Harper & Row.

COX, O. (1959) The Foundations of Capitalism. New York: Philosophical Library.

CREAMER, D., S. DOBROVOLSKY, and I. BERNSTEIN (1960) Capital in Manufacturing and Mining. Princeton, NJ: Princeton Univ. Press.

CURRY, L. (1969) Rail Routes South. Lexington: Univ. of Kentucky Press.

DUNCAN, B. and S. LIEBERSON (1970) Metropolis and Region in Transition. Beverly Hills: Sage Publications.

DUNCAN, O. D. et al. (1960) Metropolis and Region. Baltimore: Johns Hopkins Univ. Press.

DUNN, E. (1954) The Location of Agricultural Production. Gainesville: Univ. of Florida Press.

FOGEL, R. (1964) Railroads in American Economic Growth: Essays in Econometric History. Baltimore: Johns Hopkins Univ. Press.

FOGELSON, R. (1967) The Fragmented Metropolis. Cambridge, MA: Harvard Univ. Press.

FONER, P. (1941) Business and Slavery: The New York Merchants and the Irrepressible Conflict. Chapel Hill: Univ. of North Carolina Press.

FRIEDRICH, C. J. [trans.] (1928) Alfred Weber's Theory of the Location of Industries. Chicago: Univ. of Chicago Press.

FUCHS, V. (1968) The Service Economy. New York: National Bureau of Economic Research.

GATES, P. (1960) The Farmer's Age: Agriculture, 1815-1860. New York: Holt, Rinehart & Winston.

GLAAB, C. (1967) Kansas City and the Railroads. Madison: State Historical Society of Wisconsin.

––– and T. BROWN (1967) A History of Urban America. New York: Macmillan.

GOTTMAN, J. (1961) Megalopolis. Cambridge, MA: MIT Press.

GRAS, N.S.B. (1922) An Introduction to Economic History. New York: Harper & Row.

GREEN, C. (1965) American Cities in the Growth of the Nation. New York: Harper & Row.

GREENHUT, M. (1954) Plant Location in Theory and Practice. Chapel Hill: Univ. of North Carolina Press.

HALL, M. (1959) Made In New York. Cambridge, MA: Harvard Univ. Press.

HALL, P. [ed.] (1966) Von Thunen's Isolated State. Oxford: Pergamon.

HANNAH, F. (1959) State Income Differentials: 1919-1954. Durham, NC: Duke Univ. Press.

HARRISON, B. (1974) Urban Economic Development. Washington, DC: Urban Institute.

HARVEY, D. (1973) Social Justice and the City. Baltimore: Johns Hopkins Univ. Press.

HAWLEY, A. (1950) Human Ecology. New York: Ronald Press.

HILTON, G. and J. DUE (1960) The Electric Interurban Railways in America. Palo Alto: Stanford Univ. Press.

HOOVER, C. and B. U. RATCHFORD (1951) Economic Resources and Policies of the South. New York: Macmillan.

HOOVER, E. (1937) Location Theory and the Shoe and Leather Industry. Cambridge, MA: Harvard Univ. Press.

ISARD, W. (1956) Location and Space Economy. Cambridge, MA: MIT Press.

JACOBS, J. (1969) The Economy of Cities. New York: Random House.

KAIN, L. (1966) The Waterfall That Built a City. St. Paul: Minnesota Historical Society.

KETTELL, T. (1965) Southern Wealth and Northern Profits. Montgomery: Univ. of Alabama Press.

KIRKLAND, E. (1961) Industry Comes of Age. Chicago: Holt, Rinehart & Winston.

KUZNETS, S. (1961) Capital in the American Economy. Princeton, NJ: Princeton Univ. Press.

–––, A. MILLER, and R. EASTERLIN (1960) Population Redistribution and Economic Growth: United States, 1870-1950. Philadelphia: American Philosophical Society.

LICHTENBERG, R. (1960) One Tenth of a Nation. Cambridge, MA: Harvard Univ. Press.

LIVINGOOD, J. W. (1947) The Philadelphia-Baltimore Trade Rivalry. Harrisburg: Pennsylvania Historical and Museum Commission.

LOSCH, A. (1954) The Economics of Location. New Haven, CT: Yale Univ. Press.

LOWE, A. (1965) On Economic Knowledge. New York: Harper & Row.

LUBOVE, R. (1969) Twentieth Century Pittsburgh. New York: John Wiley.

MACHLUP, F. (1949) The Basing Point System. Philadelphia: Blakiston.

MADDOX, J. et al. (1967) The Advancing South. New York: Twentieth Century Fund.

MANTOUX, P. (1961) The Industrial Revolution in the Eighteenth Century. New York: Harper & Row.

MARTIN, R. (1939) National Income of the United States, 1799-1938. New York: National Bureau of Economic Research.

McKENZIE, R. (1933) The Metropolitan Community. New York: McGraw-Hill.

McGLAUGHLIN, G. (1938) Growth of American Manufacturing Areas. Pittsburgh: Univ. of Pittsburgh Press.

MITCHELL, B. (1930) The Industrial Revolution in the South. Baltimore: Johns Hopkins Univ. Press.

MUTH, R. (1969) Cities and Housing. Chicago: Univ. of Chicago Press.

MYRDALL, G. (1957) Economic Theory and Underdeveloped Regions. New York: Harper & Row.

National Emergency Council (1938) Report On The Economic Conditions of the South. Washington, DC: U.S. Government Printing Office.

NORTH, D. (1961) The Economic Growth of the United States, 1790-1860. Englewood Cliffs, NJ: Prentice-Hall.

ODUM, H. (1936) Southern Regions of the United States. Chapel Hill: Univ. of North Carolina Press.

PERLOFF, H. et al. (1960) Regions, Resources, and Economic Growth. Baltimore: Johns Hopkins Univ. Press.

PRED, A. (1973) Urban Growth and the Circulation of Information. Cambridge, MA: Harvard Univ. Press.

––– (1966) The Spatial Dynamics of U.S. Urban Industrial Growth, 1800-1914. Cambridge, MA: MIT Press.

ROSTOW, W. W. (1978) The World Economy: History and Prospect. Austin: Univ. of Texas Press.

––– (1960) The Stages of Economic Growth. Cambridge, MA: Cambridge Univ. Press.

RUBIN, J. (1961) Canal or Railroad. Philadelphia: American Philosophical Society.

SALE, K. (1975) Power Shift. New York: Random House.

SCHUMPETER, J. (1962) Capitalism, Socialism, and Democracy. New York: Harper & Row.

SEGAL, M. (1960) Wages in the Metropolis. Cambridge, MA: Harvard Univ. Press.

SENNETT, R. (1969) Classic Essays on the Culture of Cities. New York: Appleton-Century-Crofts.

SHANNON, F. (1945) The Farmer's Last Frontier. New York: Farrar & Rinehart.

STOCKING, G. (1954) Basing Point Pricing and Regional Development. Chapel Hill: Univ. of North Carolina Press.

TAYLOR, G. (1964) The Transportation Revolution. New York: Holt, Rinehart & Winston.

THOMPSON, W. (1963) A Preface to Urban Economics. Baltimore: Johns Hopkins Univ. Press.

ULLMAN, E., M. DACEY, and H. BRODSKY (1969) The Economic Base of American Cities. Seattle: Center for Urban and Regional Research.

VANCE, R. (1945) All These People. Chapel Hill: Univ. of North Carolina Press.

VEBLEN, T. (1939) Imperial Germany and the Industrial Revolution. New York: Viking.

WADE, R. (1959) The Urban Frontier. Chicago: Univ. of Chicago Press.

WARNER, S. B. (1972) Streetcar Suburbs. New York: Atheneum.

WEBER, A. F. (1963) The Growth of Cities in the Nineteenth Century. Ithaca, NY: Cornell Univ. Press.

WOODWARD, C. V. (1951) The Origins of the New South, 1877-1913. Baton Rouge: Louisiana State Univ. Press.

ARTICLES

ALCHIAN, A. (1950) "Uncertainty, evolution, and economic theory." Journal of Political Economy 58, 3: 211-221.

ALEXANDER, J. (1954) "The basic-nonbasic concept of urban economic functions." Economic Geography 30, 3: 246-261.

––– (1952) "Industrial expansion in the United States." Economic Geography 28, 2: 128-142.

ALLMAN, T. D. (1978) "The urban crisis leaves town and moves to the suburbs." Harpers (December): 41-56.

ANDERSON, G. (1943) "The South and the problems of post-Civil War finance." Journal of Southern History 9, 2: 181-185.

BARTON, F. (1942) "The freight rate structure and the distribution of defense contracts." Southern Economic Journal 8, 2: 122-133.

BAER, W. (1976) "On the death of cities." Public Interest 45 (Fall): 3-19.

BERGE, W. (1947) "Monopoly and the south." Southern Economic Journal 13, 4: 360-369.

BERRY, B. (1962) "Cities as systems within systems of cities." Papers and Proceedings of the Regional Science Association 13: 147-164.

――― and Y. COHEN (1973) "Decentralization of commerce and industry: the restructuring of metropolitan America," pp. 431-455 in L. Masotti and J. Hadden (eds.) The Urbanization of the Suburbs. Beverly Hills: Sage Publications.

BERRY, B. and W. L. GARRISON (1958) "A note on central place theory and the range of a good." Economic Geography 34, 4: 304-311.

BIGGAR, J. (1979) "The sunning of America: migration to the sunbelt." Population Bulletin 34, 1 (Washington, DC: Population Reference Bureau, Inc.).

BLUMENFELD, H. (1955) "The economic base of the metropolis." Journal of the American Institute of Planners 21 (Fall): 114-132.

BORCHERT, J. (1967) "American metropolitan evolution." Geographical Review 57, 4: 301-332.

BRODSKY, H. (1970) "Residential land and improvement values in a central city." Land Economics 46 (August): 229-247.

Business Week (1976) "A counterattack in the war between the states." June 21: 71.

――― (1976) "Brain drain: a worry for New England." October 25: 32.

――― (1976) "Financing troubles for VW's new plant." July 5: 26.

――― (1976) "No welcome mat for unions in the Sunbelt." May 17: 109-110.

CADWALLADER, M. (1959) "The cybernetic analysis of change in complex social organizations." American Journal of Sociology 65, 2: 154-157.

CALLENDAR, G. (1902) "The early transportation and banking enterprises of the states in relation to the growth of corporations." Quarterly Journal of Economics 17, 1: 111-162.

CHINITZ, B. (1972) "New York and Pittsburgh: contrasts in agglomeration." American Economic Review 51 (May): 272-289.

――― and R. DUSSANSKY (1972) "The patterns of urbanization within regions of the U.S." Urban Studies 9, 3: 289-298.

CLARK, J. M. (1938) "Basing point methods of price quotation." Canadian Journal of Economics and Political Science 4, 4: 477-489.

CLARK, T. (1948) "Imperfect competition in the southern retail trade after 1865." Journal of Economic History 3 (Supplement): 38-47.

――― (1946) "The furnishing and supply system in southern agriculture since 1865." Journal of Southern History 12, 1: 24-44.

COPELAND, M. (1940-1941) "Competing products and monopolistic competition." Quarterly Journal of Economics 55, 1: 1-35.

COYLE, D. (1937) "The south's unbalanced budget." Virginia Quarterly Review 13, 2: 192-208.

CRANMER, H. J. (1960) "Canal investment, 1815-1860," pp. 547-564 in W. Parker (ed.) Trends in the American Economy in the Nineteenth Century. Princeton, NJ: Princeton Univ. Press.

CROWLEY, R. (1973) "Reflections and further evidence on population size and industrial diversification." Urban Studies 10, 1: 91-94.

DANHOFF, C. (1964) "Four decades of thought on the south's economic problems," pp. 7-68 in M. Greenhut and W. T. Whitman (eds.) Essays in Southern Economic Development. Chapel Hill: Univ. of North Carolina Press.

——— (1944) "Agricultural technology to 1880," pp. 113-140 in H. Williamson (ed.) The Growth of the American Economy. New York: Prentice-Hall.

——— (1941) "Farm making costs and the safety valve: 1815-1860." Journal of Political Economy 49, 3: 317-359.

DEWEY, D. (1955) "A reappraisal of F.O.B. pricing and freight absorption." Southern Economic Journal 22, 1: 48-54.

EDWARDS, C. (1949) "Geographic price formulas and concentration of economic power." Georgetown Law Journal 37, 1: 135-148.

——— (1948) "The effects of recent basing point decisions upon business practices." American Economic Review 38, 5: 828-842.

EVANS, A. (1972) "The pure theory of city size in an industrial economy." Urban Studies 9, 1: 49-77.

FELLER, I. (1971) "The urban location of U.S. invention, 1860-1910." Explorations in Entrepreneurial History 8, 3: 285-304.

FETTER, F. (1948) "Exit basing point pricing." American Economic Review 38, 5: 815-827.

——— (1937) "The new plea for basing point monopoly." Journal of Political Economy 45, 5: 577-605.

——— (1924) "The economic law of market areas." Quarterly Journal of Economics 38, 4: 520-592.

FISHLOW, A. (1964) "Ante-bellum interregional trade reconsidered." American Economic Review 54 (May): 352-364.

FLEETWOOD, B. (1979) "The new elite and an urban renaissance." New York Times Magazine (January 14): 16-22, 26, 34-35.

FRIEDMAN, J. (1958) "Economy and space: a review article." Economic Development and Cultural Change 6, 3: 249-255.

GALLMAN, R. (1960) "Commodity output, 1839-1899," pp. 13-71 in W. Parker (ed.) Trends in the American Economy in the Nineteenth Century. Princeton, NJ: National Bureau of Economic Research.

GLAAB, C. (1965) "The historian and the American city: a bibliographic survey," pp. 53-80 in P. Hauser and L. Schnore (eds.) The Study of Urbanization. New York: Macmillan.

GOODRICH, C. (1950) "The revulsion against internal improvements." Journal of Economic History 10, 2: 145-169.

——— (1949) "Local planning of internal improvements." Political Science Quarterly 64, 4: 355-387.

——— and H. SEGAL (1953) "Baltimore's aid to railroads—a survey in the municipal planning of internal improvements." Journal of Economic History 13, 2: 2-35.

GORDON, D. (1977) "Class struggle and the stages of American urban development," pp. 55-82 in D. Perry and A. Watkins (eds.) The Rise of the Sunbelt Cities. Beverly Hills: Sage Publications.

GREENBERG, M. and N. VALENTE (1975) "Recent economic trends in major northeastern metropolises," pp. 77-99 in G. Sternlieb and J. Hughes (eds.) Post Industrial America: Metropolitan Decline and Interregional Job Shifts. New Brunswick, NJ: Center for Urban Policy Research.

HAIG, R. (1926) "The assignment of activities to areas in urban regions." Quarterly Journal of Economics 40, 4: 402-434.

HARRIS, C. (1954) "The market as a factor in the localization of industry in the United States." Annals of the Association of American Geographers 44 (December): 315-348.

——— (1943) "A functional classification of cities in the United States." Geographical Review 33, 1: 86-99.

HARRISON, B. and S. KANTER (1976) "The great state robbery." Working Papers for a New Society 4 (Spring): 57-66.

HASKING, R. (1968) "Planter and cotton factor in the old south," pp. 92-112 in A. Chandler and L. Galambos (eds.) The Changing Economic Order. New York: Harcourt Brace Jovanovich.

HEATH, M. (1950) "Public railroad construction and the development of private enterprise in the south before 1861." Journal of Economic History 10 (Supplement): 40-53.

——— (1946) "The uniform class rate decision and its implications for southern economic development." Southern Economic Journal 12, 3: 213-237.

HIGGS, R. (1971) "American inventiveness, 1870-1920." Journal of Political Economy 79, 3: 661-667.

HILDEBRAND, G. and A. MACE (1950) "The employment multiplier in an expanding industrial market: Los Angeles county, 1940-1947." Review of Economics and Statistics 32, 3: 241-249.

HOOVER, C. (1949) "Economy of the south." Report of the Joint Committee on the impact of federal policies on the economy of the south. Washington, DC: U.S. Government Printing Office.

HOOVER, E. (1964) "Pittsburgh takes stock of itself," pp. 53-65 in B. Chinitz (eds.) City and Suburb. Englewood Cliffs, NJ: Prentice-Hall.

——— (1935) "Spatial price discrimination." Review of Economic Studies 4, 3: 182-191.

HOTELLING, H. (1929) "Stability in competition." Economic Journal 39 (March): 41-57.

HUND, J. (1959) "Electronics," pp. 241-325 in M. Hall (ed.) Made in New York. Cambridge, MA: Harvard Univ. Press.

ISARD, W. (1948) "Some locational factors in the iron and steel industry since the early nineteenth century." Journal of Political Economy 56, 3: 203-217.

JOHNSON, W. (1949) "The restricted incidence of basing point pricing on regional development." Georgetown Law Journal 37, 1: 149-165.

KAIN, J. (1968) "The distribution and movement of jobs and industry," pp. 1-43 in J. Wilson (ed.) The Metropolitan Enigma. Cambridge, MA: Harvard Univ. Press.

KAYSEN, C. (1949) "Basing point pricing and public policy." Quarterly Journal of Economics 63, 3: 289-314.

KRYZMOWSKI, R. (1928) "A graphical presentation of Thunen's theory of intensity." Journal of Farm Economics 10, 4: 461-482.

LAMPARD, E. (1968) "The evolving system of cities in the United States," pp. 81-140 in H. Perloff and L. Wingo (eds.) Issues in Urban Economics. Baltimore: Johns Hopkins Univ. Press.

––– (1960) "Regional economic development, 1870-1950," pp. 107-292 in H. Perloff et al. (eds.) Regions, Resources, and Economic Growth. Baltimore: Johns Hopkins Univ. Press.

––– (1955) "The history of cities in the economically advanced areas." Economic Development and Cultural Change 3, 2: 81-136.

LEIGH, A. (1946) "Von Thunen's theory of distribution and the advent of marginal analysis." Journal of Political Economy 54, 6: 481-502.

LERNER, A and H. W. SINGER (1937) "Some notes on duopoly and spatial competition." Journal of Political Economy 45, 2: 145-186.

LEWIS, W. A. (1958) "Economic development with unlimited supplies of labor," pp. 400-450 in A. N. Agarwala and S. P. Singh (eds.) The Economics of Underdevelopment. New York: Oxford Univ. Press.

LONG, N. (1971) "The city as reservation." Public Interest 25 (Fall): 22-38.

LOTCHIN, R. (1972) "San Francisco: the patterns of chaos and growth," pp. 143-163 in K. Jackson and S. Schultz (eds.) Cities in American History. New York: Knopf.

LUKERMAN, F. (1966) "Empirical expressions of nodality and hierarchy in a circulation manifold." East Lakes Geographer 2, 1: 17-44.

MADDEN, C. (1958) "Some temporal aspects of the growth of cities in the United States." Economic Development and Cultural Change 6, 2: 143-170.

MARBURG, T. (1960) "Income originating in trade," pp. 327-336 in W. Parker (eds.) Trends in the American Economy in the Nineteenth Century. Princeton, NJ: National Bureau of Economic Research.

MARUYAMA, M. (1963) "The second cybernetics: deviation amplifying mutual causal processes." General Systems 8, 2: 233-241.

MATILLA, J. and W. THOMPSON (1955) "The measurement of the economic base of the metropolitan area." Land Economics 31, 3: 215-228.

MAYER, H. (1969) "Making a living in cities: the urban economic base." Journal of Geography 68, 2: 70-87.

MILLS, E. (1970) "Urban density gradients." Urban Studies 7, 1: 5-20.

MOLLENKOPF, J. (1975) "The post-war politics of urban development." Politics and Society 5, 3: 247-296.

MORRISSETT, I. (1957) "The economic structure of American cities." Papers and Proceedings of the Regional Science Association 4: 239-258.

NELSON, H. (1970) "The form and structure of cities: urban growth patterns," pp. 101-110 in R. Putnam, F. Taylor, and P. Kettle (eds.) A Geography of Urban Places. Toronto: Methuen.

––– (1955) "A service classification of U.S. cities." Economic Geography 31, 2: 189-210.

NETTLES, C. (1930) "The economic relations of Boston, Philadelphia, and New York." Journal of Economic and Business History 3, 2: 185-215.

New York Times (1977) "Pittsburgh revamped and revitalized sheds its steel town image: April 16: 27.

––– (1976) "Cut business taxes New York City urged." December 13.

––– (1976) "State's commerce chief asks fiscal shift to right." February 2.

NORTH, D. (1955) "Location theory and regional economic growth." Journal of Political Economy 63, 3: 243-258.

PEET, J. R. (1969) "The spatial expansion of commercial agriculture in the nineteenth century: A Von Thunen interpretation." Economic Geography 45, 4: 283-301.

PERRY, D. and A. WATKINS (1980) "The urban renaissance for business." The Nation (March 1): 236-239.

PERSKY, J. (1973) "The south: a colony at home." Southern Exposure 1, 2: 14-22.

PFOUTS, W. R. and E. CURTIS (1958) "Limitations of the economic base analysis." Social Forces 36, 4: 303-310.

POTTER, D. (1947) "The historical development of eastern-southern freight rate relationships." Law and Contemporary Problems 12, 3: 416-448.

PRED, A. (1971) "Large city interdependence and the pre-electronic diffusion of innovations in the U.S." Geographical Analysis 3, 2: 165-181.

Progressive (1979) "Urban renaissance: the reality beneath the glitter." January: 26-47.

RAE, J. (1944) "Federal land grants in aid of canals." Journal of Economic History 4, 2: 167-177.

REINEMANN, M. (1970) "The pattern and distribution of manufacturing in the Chicago area," pp. 111-116 in R. Putnam, F. Taylor, and P. Kettle (eds.) A Geography of Urban Places. Toronto: Methuen.

RODGERS, A. (1952) "Industrial inertia: a major factor in the location of the steel industry in the United States." Geographical Review 42, 1: 56-66.

ROSS, E. (1944) "The emergence of agricultural regionalism," pp. 379-410 in H. F. Williamson (ed.) The Growth of the American Economy. New York: Prentice-Hall.

RUBIN, J. (1967) "Urban growth and regional development," pp. 3-21 in D. T. Gilchrist (ed.) The Growth of the Seaport Cities, 1790-1825. Charlottesville: Univ. of Virginia Press.

RUTTAN, V. (1955) "Industrial progress and rural stagnation in the new south." Social Forces 34, 2: 114-117.

SCHLEBECKER, J. (1960) "The world metropolis and the history of American agriculture." Journal of Economic History 20, 2: 187-208.

SCHMIDT, L. (1939) "Internal commerce and the development of the national economy before 1860." Journal of Political Economy 47, 6: 798-822.

SCHNORE, L. (1964) "Urban structure and suburban selectivity." Demography 1, 1: 164-176.

––– (1962) "City suburban income differentials in metropolitan areas." American Sociological Review 27, 2: 262-255.

SMITH, D. M. (1966) "A theoretical framework for geographical studies of industrial location." Economic Geography 42, 2: 95-114.

SMITHIES, A. (1942) "Aspects of the basing point system." American Economic Review 32, 4: 705-725.

––– (1941) "Optimum location in spatial competition." Journal of Political Economy 49, 3: 423-439.

STARR, R. (1976) "Making New York smaller." New York Times Magazine (November 14): 32-33, 99-106.

STERNLIEB, G. (1971) "The city as sandbox." Public Interest 25 (Fall): 14-21.

STEWART, C. (1959) "Economic base dynamics." Land Economics 35, 4: 327-336.

STIGLER, G. (1951) "The division of labor is limited by the extent of the market." Journal of Political Economy 59, 3: 185-193.

——— (1949) "A theory of delivered price systems." American Economic Review 39, 6: 1143-1159.

STOLPER, W. (1955) "Spatial order and the economic growth of cities." Economic Development and Cultural Change 3, 2: 137-147.

TAYLOR, G. (1967) "American urban growth preceding the railway age." Journal of Economic History 27, 3: 309-339.

THOMPSON, W. (1975) "Economic process and employment problems in declining metropolitan areas," pp. 187-196 in G. Sternlieb and J. Hughes (eds.) Post Industrial America: Metropolitan Decline and Interregional Job Shifts. New Brunswick, NJ: Center for Urban Policy Research.

——— (1968) "Internal and external factors in the development of urban economies," pp. 43-62 in H. Perloff and L. Wingo (eds.) Issues In Urban Economics. Baltimore: Johns Hopkins Univ. Press.

TIEBOUT, C. (1960) "Community income multipliers: a population growth model." Journal of Regional Science 2, 1: 75-84.

——— (1957) "Location theory, empirical evidence, and economic evolution." Papers and Proceedings of the Regional Science Association 3: 74-86.

ULLMAN, E. (1968) "Minimum requirements after a decade: a critique and a reappraisal." Economic Geography 44, 4: 364-369.

——— (1958) "Regional development and the geography of concentration." Papers and Proceedings of the Regional Science Association 4: 179-198.

——— and M. DACEY (1960) "The minimum requirements approach to the urban economic base." Papers and Proceedings of the Regional Science Association 6: 175-199.

U.S. Congress (1947) "Study of the agricultural and economic problems of the cotton belt." Subcommittee on Cotton of the Committee on Agriculture. 80th Cong., 1st Sess., July 7-8.

VANCE, J. (1960) "Labor shed, employment field, and dynamic analysis in urban geography." Economic Geography 36, 3: 189-220.

Wall Street Journal (1976) "Sick cities: many municipalities lag behind the rest of the nation in recovering from economic downturn." June 16.

——— (1976) "Sick cities: municipal leaders try to cure economic ills but the medicine often worsens the ailments." June 17.

WALMSLEY, M. (1965) "The bygone electric interurban railway system." Professional Geographer 17, 1: 1-16.

WATKINS, A. (1978) "Intermetropolitan migration and the rise of the sunbelt." Social Science Quarterly 59, 3: 553-561.

WILLIAMSON, J. (1965) "Regional inequality and the process of national development: a description of the patterns." Economic Development and Cultural Change 13, 1: 3-45.

WOODBURY, C. and F. CLIFFE (1953) "Industrial location and urban redevelopment," pp. 103-288 in C. Woodbury (ed.) The Future of Cities and Urban Redevelopment. Chicago: Univ. of Chicago Press.

WRIGHT, A. J. "Recent changes in the concentration of manufacturing." Annals of the Association of American Geographers 35 (January): 144-166.

ABOUT THE AUTHOR

ALFRED J. WATKINS received his Ph.D. from the Department of Economics of the New School for Social Research and is currently Assistant Professor of Government at the University of Texas at Austin, where he teaches courses in political economy. He has coedited *The Rise of the Sunbelt Cities* with David Perry and has written numerous articles on the economic and demographic aspects of regional growth and decay. In addition, Professor Watkins has contributed several articles on urban affairs to the New York *Times, The Nation,* and *Dissent.*